LOCATIONS MENTIONED IN THE BOOK

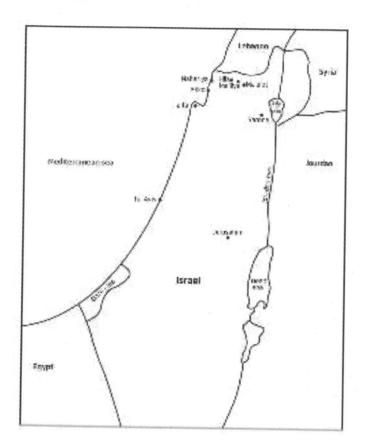

Map of Israel

ACKNOWLEDGEMENTS

I was reminded by the book's publisher that I had to thank people for their help. I responded that half of the world would be acknowledged. Many people supported me through my journey, from 2001 to the present, when I was at the bottom of the pit, ready for my fate to be accepted. Unfortunately, it is impossible to list them all.

The acknowledgement section was divided into three sections. The first acknowledges all those who supported me in my fight with illness. Without them, I would not have survived. The second part of my acknowledgements is dedicated to the many people who contributed to the fundraising effort to fund the treatment I received at a German clinic. My third acknowledgement is dedicated to those who helped me publish the book. Without them, it would not have been possible.

My older brother Arieh, Dina, and their children are to be sincerely thanked for all the support they have given me over the years. Their family has provided me with a solid, supportive, and uplifting foundation that has warmed my heart to the core. They were also the initiators and leaders of the Sarona fundraising project, which was held on the land that they own.

I'm also thankful to Izhar, my younger brother, and Irit, his partner. They played a crucial role in steering me through the critical stages of my treatment, particularly at the beginning, when so much was unknown and I was helpless.

I am grateful to my doctors and medical team for being there in my most difficult moments and in my best:
Dr. Menachem Benjamin-Shachar is the head of the medical team at Nahariya's oncology ward. Over the years, he has been a great caretaker and allowed me to have treatments that were not considered standard in the system he managed. Ann, Lily, the nursing staff, and all other nurses were wonderful and willing to do whatever was necessary with professionalism and

compassion. This helped me feel hopeful and a sense of faith, especially in the more severe cases that I encountered at the ward. Batya and her medical administrative team are to be commended for their professionalism and making it easier for me to navigate the bureaucracy associated with my treatment.

Special thanks to Dr. Avivit Neumann who is an expert on prostate cancer and was always willing to share her vast knowledge and time with me for free. She gave me the medical approval to a treatment that no other expert was willing to approve and greatly contributed to my survival.

I am also thankful to Dr. Ruthie, who generously offered to help me with all aspects of my illness, even though I was helpless and confused. She did this with unending devotion for a long period.

I am thankful to Dr. Dan Keret for helping me through this emotional and physical rollercoaster with tenderness, and amazing grace.

Thank you Dr. Raphael Robinov. He is a leading expert in oncology, and a gentle, sensitive soul. I also consulted him during difficult times, and he has given a lot of time with patience, kindness, and understanding. I still have the medical insights that he gave me at our evening meetings at home. They are invaluable in my ongoing fight against cancer.

Yoel Kotsan, my friend and mentor, is a man I am thankful for his friendship, support and willingness to help me in any situation.

Three people have I never met, I feel the need acknowledge them:
Bill Aishman, an American prostate cancer patient, instilled in my mind the need to think and act differently. The knowledge he shared with me via email is a crucial aspect of my survival.

Larry Sorenson, an Australian long-distance friend, sent me lots of information via email on how to deal with the illness. He sent me the protocol for chemotherapy and information about its beneficial effects as well as the side effects. This knowledge helped me build the strength to get the treatment I needed.

Don Cooley, an American who started and managed the virtual forum for prostate cancer patients. This forum provided endless information that I used, along with many others, for my private battle against prostate cancer. There, I met my two best friends and shared many details about my illness with them. Even though I never got to meet them in person, our friendship grew into a real intimacy.

Both Bill and Larry both died from the illness.

Ilana Levy Zihan, a neighbor and friend in Mitzpe Hila who organized the fundraiser that allowed me to receive treatment at St. George Clinic in Germany and motivated many others, is a special thanks. It is the same for Mitzpe Hila residents, including Menachem Adiel who designed a pendant to raise funds; Tami Cohen who created the graphics and needed advertisement, Ornit Bar-Zait, Alan Kantor and Eyal Tsadok who were a neighbor and good friend and many more.

The project also included the youth and hiking movements of Mitzpe Hila, and its surrounding areas.

Avi Krampa, the head of the regional council supported the council and recruited as necessary.

Apart from my family, Daniel Amit was instrumental in the development of Sarona's agricultural village. Shlomo Avraham also helped with technical aspects.

Lenny Hirsch was my friend and supported the Teva Ez fundraiser. He also helped me through the years with the disease. I was saved by his vast knowledge and wisdom about prostate cancer.

We are grateful to Ofra Elkobi for her kindness and willingness to help us collect all donations.

Bookkeeper Yossi Fadida, and CPA Effi Wildman, were volunteers to help manage the financial aspects of the project.

It is hard to not express my gratitude to the generous donors who supported me in my quest to find treatment in Germany. Some of them are still anonymous, and I haven't met many of them.

I want to thank my brother Izhar and his partner Irit for publishing this book. Without their encouragement and support, this book would not have been published. They would encourage me to keep writing even if I quit. Izhar and I met in a Rome hotel. We sat together from morning to night trying to save the book from its fate.

Rafi Hershkowitz was a good friend for 35 years. He offered to edit the first round after I told him about the adventures that had preoccupied me on our trip. Without his tireless work on the messy draft that I gave him, I doubt that the book would have been published. I am grateful to him and his wife Ora for their time and effort to organize the text they received from you.

Avivit Neumann, an oncologist, has been blessed with the unique ability to help others. We were able to overcome many obstacles on our path to publishing the book thanks to her wise advice and support.

Yosef Alkoni is a publisher who volunteered his expertise to assist me with the publishing process. I was able to overcome all the obstacles with his advice and experience.

Focus Publishing decided to publish the book because it felt that its mission was to share messages of hope with its readers.

Last but not least, I want to thank my immediate family for supporting me through the many tumultuous times that have accompanied my life over the years because of my illness. My wife Rivka and my children Orr, Bat El, and Amir, I express my gratitude and great love.

FOREWORD by DR. DAN KERET

My experience with patients with cancer is very different to that of patients with other diseases. Many want to take part in their recovery. I see how their priorities shift and how they move in a direction that will lead to recovery. They are more willing to make changes than those who don't have cancer and they do so much quicker than others. They may do this because they have to confront a threat to life, fear, and harsh stereotypes that come with the disease. You may also be unable to get the medicine you need.

Itzy Be'er is just one of them. We see the warrior fight for his life throughout this book. We follow his relentless battle against the illness to see the amazing results.

Itzy stated in his book more than once that he doesn't understand how he was so fortunate to be able to fight side-by-side with him, and gave him ideas and inspiration for his battle. One of the reasons for this mystery question is the characteristics of survivors. I explained to Itzy in one of our meetings that I believed these were the factors. I also presented them with strong reasoning to prove my faith in him.

These are seven characteristics that make survivors able to overcome seemingly impossible obstacles:

1. They don't take no for an answer.
2. They seek out help in a creative, active way.
3. They seek out others who have made it back.
4. They form effective partnerships with professionals.
5. They are not afraid to make drastic changes in their lives.

6.   They view the illness as a gift, or an opportunity.
7.   They accept the imperfections, limitations, and flaws that we all have.No doubt, the reader will find everything necessary to be a survivor in the author.

Itzy's story is an inspiration to other warriors fighting for lives. It may also help them discover their own recipe that will bring them extraordinary results.

Itzy traveled with me on many of his adventures. His willingness to do whatever it took to get relief from his illness was what impressed me most. He refused to accept help from his friends or other supporters, but he persevered and asked for it. Few of us are willing to fight for our rights. He is a strong believer in himself and his ability to find support and help. These qualities are what made him so successful.

Let's send our best wishes for him and his fight against cancer.

Dr.   Dan   Keret
ddkeret@zahav.net.il

FOREWORD   by DR. AVIVIT NEUMANN

Cancer is one of our most frightening words.

Malignant tumors were known to exist even before the advent of modern medicine. They were called "cancer" because they can grow sideways and crawl. Many facts have been discovered about how cancer spreads. It tricks the immune system, spreading to distant areas, and deceives the patient.

Many laboratories are also trying out new drugs and mechanisms in an effort to eradicate cancer.

Prostate cancer is the most common form of cancer in men over recent years. Twenty years ago, only one in twenty men was diagnosed with this kind of cancer. Today, one in six men will be affected by this disease at some time during their lives. The majority of patients with this type of tumor are in their 70s, although some have been diagnosed in their 40s.

Each patient brings their own uniqueness to the treatment. Each patient has a unique cultural background, different perspectives, and their own personality.

Itzy was a telephone call that started my relationship with him. Itzy was an extraordinary person from the beginning. I was amazed by his thirst for knowledge, meticulousness in studying the disease, his honesty, and practicality. Since the beginning of his treatments, we have kept in touch for more than eight years. Although I'm not his traditional doctor, due to the distance between Mitzpe Hila, Israel, and the center, I can guide him through the various remedial points.

Because of the advanced stage of his disease at the time of its diagnosis in 2001, I was the one to predict a dark, apocalyptic outcome, while Itzy tried his best to instill the same faith in me as he believed he could win the battle. He was correct, to my immense joy and miraculously.

Itzy's book can be a great resource for many patients, both emotionally and informatively.

Itzy's message is for all of us, patients and caregivers alike.

Enjoy your reading!
Dr. Avivit Neumann, Oncologist

PREFACE

February 2009

Twenty-two days prior to my fiftieth Birthday, on October 28, 2001, I was admitted to Nahariya Hospital. Three days later, I was diagnosed as having prostate cancer. There were many metastases in my bones, and two smaller ones in my right lung. These are called nodules. I was blinded by a black curtain that fell before me, blocking my view of the rest of my life.

Irit, my younger brother, Izhar, encouraged me to create a journal as a therapy tool. Because she knew I was interested in writing, she was able to hear some of my thoughts when I read them aloud. I was also encouraged by my naturopath to write.

She said, "Writing will help to tear apart the black curtain suddenly shut before your eyes," It is important to not let things simmer in your mind, but to let them go.

Between my initial decision to write and the execution of it, it took a few months. About two-and-a-half months after I was diagnosed with my illness and the world fell on me, I started the task of writing.

My journal entries accumulated and, seven years later, I found myself in Rome in a hotel trying to make those journal entries into books. Parts of this journal were written as a complement to the journal that I had written. Izhar, my younger brother, was there to guide me and help me as much as possible.

My personal story and battle with prostate cancer are told in the book. Although I have not fully recovered from the disease, the cancer is still present in my body. However, I lead a normal life for someone my age, which is strange considering the fact that I am also living with the cancer. Despite all odds and risks, I won the fight and I feel proud of my victory.

This book includes explanations and medical insights that I have accumulated over the past seven years, since my diagnosis as a patient with cancer. I am not a physician and the information contained herein should not be considered as a recommendation for treatment.

Richard Nixon, then President of the United States, launched a national program in 1971 to find cures for cancer. Although huge budgets were spent on research and studies, many types of cancer remain uncurable today, 45 years after the fact.

Cancer is one of many diseases that can cause uncontrolled reproduction. There are many types of cancer.

The prostate is a similar-sized gland to a chestnut. It is located in the urethra of a male and has the function to secrete some seminal fluid.

Prostate cancer occurs in the prostate gland. It can spread to other areas of the body, and even cause death if it is not treated promptly.

It usually affects men over 50 years old, but recent years have seen more cases in which the disease has been diagnosed in men younger than 50. Today, in Israel, one out six men will be diagnosed by prostate cancer at some time during their lives.

The book features many kind and professional people. Some have created pseudonyms to keep their identities private.

My family and I live in Mitzpe Hila in northern Israel. This is where we live our daily lives. Rivka is my wife and mother to my three children, Orr, Bat-El and Amir (Guri).

The Hebrew edition of the book was published for the first time in 2010. In 2017, the epilogue was added.

CHAPTER ONE

FROM THE FIELDS of SARONA

TO TEVA EZ DAIRY

Until January 2002

In 1995, my wife Rivka and Geula, her parents Shaul and Geula, took me to the United States. Dafael was a company that created agricultural technology. I was an engineer at that time. We did this to honor Rivka's parents who had never traveled abroad before. Historical accuracy dictates that Shaul was born in Poland, and lived through World War II as an infant. His entire family was killed in the Holocaust. After the war, he survived and immigrated to Israel. He never left Israel's borders again.

Shaul noticed me urinating more often than the other travelers during the trip. Shaul noticed that I was urinating more frequently than the others and recommended that I see a doctor.

When I returned to Israel, Shaul's advice was still fresh in my mind and I went to the Nahariya health clinic to see Dr. Solan, our family doctor.

Dr. Solan, a man in his 60s, has been my family physician for many years. His accent is heavy Hungarian, which gives away his heritage. His athletic physique is well-built and his tanned skin displays a serious, authoritative look. I feel comfortable confiding in him when I come to his office with any question or problem. He makes quick medical decisions. This is a big plus for someone like me, who has not been to the doctor as often before.

After hearing my complaint, the doctor sent me to have a sugar test done with the nurse. It seemed to me that it was another sign of his great skill. The nurse took blood and did the test right away. The test came back negative. The doctor was informed by her. He said to me that there was nothing to be concerned about. Go home. It's all okay. I continued my journey with a feeling of relief that confirmed the belief I had held throughout my life: I am healthy. I don't indulge in any way that could lead to any health problems. Our family doesn't have any health issues. My mother died from terminal cancer two years ago. However, I considered that a fluke and not something that could be genetic. My father had also been diagnosed with prostate cancer many years ago, but he was able to recover. These matters were not relevant to me at the time.

Retrospectively, I see that prostate cancer spreads slowly within a patient's body in the early stages. It can take several years for symptoms to appear between the initial appearance of malignant cells and the onset. Is it possible that the seeds of prostate cancer were present in me for so long. It's hard to say. Is it possible that a thorough examination would have revealed the illness in time? Although it is possible, one cannot be certain.

— ◊ —

That was the moment I made the decision to leave the nest I had occupied for 18 years. There was a high level of success in my work. We spent a lot of time marketing the systems that we had developed in overseas. As part of this marketing activity, we wrote many technical proposals. I also had been to other countries several times. However, I didn't feel the same joy and satisfaction as when I was there earlier.

In my mid-forties, I felt a strong desire for a change in the direction of my professional life. I was ready to move on from my old home and make my own path, and take control of my destiny. These were signs of a midlife crisis. It was my last chance. In just a few years I would have turned fifty. After fifty you can't start a new career that requires physical and mental stamina. I thought, "It's now or never," just like Elvis said in his song. I didn't want to become redundant to the system in a few years, like a colleague of mine in his fifties.

I was also offered a partnership opportunity with Teva Ez, a Ben-Ami dairy that makes goat cheese.

I was born in Sarona, Lower Galilee and raised by a family of sheepherders. I am the middle of three brothers. As a child and young adult, taking care of the family herd was an important part of my life. My father was a very hard worker and my brothers and I helped him a lot with the raising of the sheep and milking them. To entice the sheep to come in, we put them in a Machlov2. Once most of the sheep were in the Machlov, we would quickly pull out the stubborn ones and place their heads inside. This would prevent them from pulling their heads out and disrupting the milking process. Once the sheep were settled, we would set up low wooden stools and use a tin bucket to manually milk each sheep. Once the bucket was full, we would strain the milk using a cloth to make a 30 liter pot. Arieh, my older brother, continues the family tradition by raising sheep today. While modern industrial methods are available today, the milking process still requires one-on-one interaction with each sheep.

Sometimes, one of us would lead a herd to its pastures. Sarona, an agricultural community, is situated on a hilly area overlooking a valley. Most of the grazing land is down valley's inclines. As a child, I often found myself working with the sheep family for quite a while. The summer saw the herd being led before the heat sets in and returning home at ten to take a break. To quench their thirst, the sheep would run to the pen. Winter meant that the departure and return would occur later. Two main challenges faced by herders were to get the sheep to eat enough during grazing. To do this, we had to take them to the pasture and slow them down so that they could concentrate on grazing. The second was to ensure that the herd returned home intact. Many times, a small number of sheep would wander off from the herd and go to a different meadow. I would quickly run to the group that was deviating and then send it back to my herd.

I was thrilled to be able to manufacture goat's milk products. It was a return to my childhood. In addition to the excitement, I knew my dairy knowledge would be a significant advantage in this new occupation. My mother would make a loaf of semi-hard cheese from fresh milk when she was feeling the urge. Although it has been many decades since then, I still enjoy the delicious flavor of that cheese in my mouth.

The art of making goat's cheese and goat milk is romantic. Goat milk is very similar to mother's milk in composition and has properties that surpass those of cow's. It may have healing properties, such as the ability to heal wounds in babies' lips. Its fat molecules, which are smaller than those found in cow's milk, don't stay in the body for as long and are eliminated by the secretion. It is therefore easier to digest.

All of this was connected to my desire to make a career change. I wanted to quit my job and find something simpler, less tech-savvy, and more in line with my personality.

However, there are reasons to not take such a step.

The financial gamble and the fear of failure was the first reason.

Rivka and I both wanted to go on a sabbatical. Dafael allowed me to take a sabbatical as part of my job. Eligible employees could choose to work in academia or in a technology-related industry during such a year. The employee's sabbatical was usually taken abroad so that the family could move with him. Between 1987 and 1988, our first sabbatical took place in the beautiful city of Corvallis in Oregon. Although it was a positive, routine-breaking experience for our family, there were some bumps along the way. I was now eligible to take another sabbatical.

Fear of joining a partnership was the third reason. Although I was able to get positive feedback from my potential partner, I didn't know him well enough to be certain about his ability to work with me.

Ironically, Dror, my future partner, had died from cancer in his twenties. I discovered this only a few years later. Although he had undergone extensive chemotherapy, he was still in good health after twenty years. I was his partner at the time and I realized that I might not have signed up for a partnership had I known.

Shaul, my father in law, was able to summarize everything in one sentence and advised me to secure my status in Dror's plot in the village.

Ilana, a close friend and neighbor, advised me not to seek the title of company owner. Although it sounds very prestigious, it is fraught with difficulties in reality. She said, "Do not sacrifice your health for this." An economist from my former job advised me about financial matters.

As part of Mati, I also hired a consultant.3 This consultant helped me to understand the meanings of the data. Based on the data, we created a business plan that showed the timeframe needed to make the company financially viable under certain assumptions.

It was difficult for me to decide whether I should join the partnership. I debated it for quite some time. It was difficult to come up with a mathematical equation that would give me an unambiguous answer. I also realized there was some gambling involved in this decision. It was a major shift in my career, which would have a profound impact on my family's lives.

Rivka was quite liberal in her approach and did not object to me taking this step. However, she preferred that I remain at Dafael with all its economic security and the sabbatical available to me, which would likely escape us if we left. Rivka is a natural communicator and can express herself in her own way. However, she believes that it is important to live and let live.

I decided to plunge into the cold water and follow my instincts. Arabs have a saying "Fil barakeh Bel charakeh," which means "There is blessing within the movement." I was ready to move on. So, in late 1995 I became an owner of Teva Ez dairy and a partner in the company. This is a goat cheese producer in Ben-Ami near Nahariya.

I learned about the various aspects of cheese production and how to market and sell it. Although my agricultural background helped me understand the milk supply process to the dairy farm, the manufacturing, selling and marketing aspects were new to me.

My first lessons were about the obstacles, which were numerous. In Israel, the cheese market is saturated. There is plenty of cheese available. Every manufacturer must sell their product despite having many competitors. The challenge for small manufacturers is even greater. He must compete against larger manufacturers for the consumer's attention and be able to play against the big guys.

Dror and me made some important decisions during our partnership that helped us manage the business. Our first decision was to expand our dairy and increase our manufacturing capabilities. We were unable to increase the dairy's production because of its small production area.

We couldn't introduce the latest technologies to withstand the fierce competition.

We expanded the existing facility to make it more spacious.

Construction took about six months. Although the facility was impressive and looked great, we were left with a lot of financial debt. That was when I started to feel awful. I was experiencing pain in my pelvis, making it difficult to walk. Nitza, Dror's wife and a professional physiotherapist recommended some physiotherapy exercises. I followed her instructions, but the exercises didn't help.

We also realized that our independent marketing organization could not be continued in the existing structure because the large chain stores weren't interested in working with small-scale suppliers. We knew we needed to partner with a strategic organization that was actively involved in this sector. After looking at all the options, we decided to partner with Gad Dairies for distribution and marketing. We also stopped using independent distribution. When we were at crossroads, the owner of Gad Dairies offered to lend us his marketing and distribution system. Their partnership is still strong today.

---

2 *Machlov is a machine that confines the sheep while they're being milked.*
3 Framework to foster entrepreneurship, which supports entrepreneurs and grassroots initiatives.

CHAPTER TWO
THE NOOSE BEGINS TIGHTENING

Mid-January 2002

In October 2000, I felt sickly. My body temperature fluctuated for many days. I felt weak and had terrible night sweats. A mobile blood donation unit called Magen David Adom by the Red Cross of Israel arrived in my neighborhood one day. As usual, I went to my local blood bank to donate blood. I had to complete a questionnaire before I could donate blood. It asked me whether or not I experienced night sweats. When I answered "yes", I knew something was wrong.

Dr. Solan was able to help me. After obtaining the results of his blood tests, he told me that there was nothing to be concerned and that I was in good health. He did not recommend any tests related to prostate cancer. As I said, Dr. Solan has a charismatic personality, so it was easy for me to believe everything was okay. I felt that I could trust him and that the troubling matter was not of any special significance. He later told me that he didn't send me for a prostatic exam because I was too young. I was 39 years old at the time. Israel's establishment recommends that prostate cancer screenings begin at the age of 50. It was easy to believe that he was right, as the weakness and fever had disappeared.

Six months later, I felt pain in my right side hip joint. Ma'alot's orthopedist examined me and sent me for Xrays. After reviewing the Xrays, he informed me that I had a slight wear to the joint and recommended physiotherapy. I asked him about the implications of this wear and he replied that it was quite common for my age. I saw physiotherapy twice. I was taught a variety of exercises by the physiotherapist to improve my hip joint condition. As she instructed, I practiced at my home. The pain subsided at some point. I felt that the physiotherapy was working and the matter was resolved.

A few minutes later, however, I felt a new pain in my left upper back. I

I didn't know that these two pains could be linked. I saw Dr. M. Gabriel again, a well-known orthopedist who was also the assistant director of a hospital. He sent me for an Xray. The same afternoon, I received the results from him. His diagnosis was the same as the one from the previous doctor. It was a wear in the joint caused by age. He recommended that I swim backstrokes. I wondered, "What's the deal?" My bones could be wearing so badly that it causes me pain. Is this where all the pain is coming from, at forty-nine? I didn't like swimming so I decided to give up. I had two-kg weights at home and decided to begin training with them. I tried to mimic the movements of backstrokes. I stood in front of the large mirror in my bedroom and tried to imitate the movements of backstrokes. I had one weight in each hand. I was required to follow the doctor's instructions and increase the wear in my joints.

As the days passed, the pain began to subside. Although I believed things were settled once again, in October 2001 I felt terrible again. I felt weak and fatigued, with more pain in my left upper back and pelvis. I had difficulty walking and found it difficult to climb stairs. My limping got worse from one day to another. After returning from work, I would take a hot shower and then go to bed. I felt some relief from the hot water.

I met an acquaintance from the community when I was limping. She asked me half-jokingly if I had been run over by a truck. When my illness was discovered and we met again, she joked half-jokingly that a truck had run me over.

Dr. Solan was again my doctor. Dr. Solan examined me and found that my first suspicion was that there was inflammation in my joints. He prescribed Vioxx, which is a medication that helps relieve joint pain.

Vioxx was an extremely popular drug up until 2004. Vioxx is a member of the NSAID (nonsteroidal-anti-inflammatory drug) class. It's used to treat joint inflammation and other types pain. Medical studies later showed that Vioxx had an effect on heart attack risk in people who had taken it for a long period of time. The drug was recalled in 2004 after it caused major scandal in America. This was the largest recall of any medical drug in history. Celebrex, a drug belonging to the same family, was found to increase longevity in cancer patients.

This could be related to Dr. Schreiber's argument in Anticancer: A New Way of Life, that inflammations are a catalyst in the growth of cancer cells. I don't know.

My condition did not improve and it was getting worse. The pain got worse and was unbearable. It became difficult to walk and it was hard for me to sleep at night. Rivka used all her strength to assist me. At bedtime, she brought me a Japanese miracle ointment. Although the ointment did help, it was only temporary.

I told Dr. Solan that I didn't feel the drug was working. I was sent to continue my bloodwork. It took me two weeks to receive the results. I tried to do it as quickly as possible. I had a bad feeling and asked the doctor if he could speed up my results. I was told by the doctor that he couldn't and that everything is fine.

I explained to him that I felt my condition was getting worse each day. He replied with his authoritative tone and Hungarian accent: "What's your problem?" Your back is hurting so you have difficulty climbing stairs. You're still walking. You're working. It's not the end.

Rivka gave me some great advice and Dr. Solan was not helping, so I sought a second opinion. She was seventy-five meters tall (four feet nine), and had wits, knowledge and compassion that far exceeded her height. She was a friend for many years, and we had benefited from her experience and knowledge in times of need. She did a quick checkup on me and advised that I do a bone scan.

Although I didn't know much about the examination at the time, I booked my first appointment. The appointment was set for Wednesday, October 17, 2001 at 3:00 pm, ten days after my last visit with Dr. Solan. The exam was performed at the Nahariya Hospital Institute of Nuclear Medicine. A radioactive substance was injected into the vein of my arm before the exam. I was instructed to drink lots of water in order to get clearer results. The technician placed me on an automated bed that moved around the scanner, and it looked almost like a large wheel. The technician told me to "Be well" after the scan. This further confirmed my suspicions that I wasn't well or, in other words, sick. In my case, those two well-wish words that are usually spoken randomly seemed like a bad sign. Still, I felt strangely relieved. I felt somehow relieved that there was some clue to help me decipher what terrible thing had taken place in my body.

A bone scan is an imaging procedure that attempts to detect bone-related issues. Before the scan, a radioactive substance is administered to the body. To ensure that the radioactive substance does not enter the bloodstream, the patient is instructed to drink water. The scanner actually maps the body's concentration of radioactive substances. Many blood vessels can develop rapidly and simultaneously in unnatural ways if there is a tumor growing. These areas are where a lot of radioactive substances concentrate. One can see the black spot in the scan. This is a sign that something is wrong. It is known as "absorption" in the medical world. If it is detected, then it means that there is a high chance of cancer metastasis. Angiogenesis is the rapid growth of these blood vessels. (angio = blood vessels; genesis = creation. They provide blood and oxygen to cancer cells, allowing them to develop rapidly.

Many studies have been conducted to try to stop the development of blood vessels (antiangiogenesis). This will help to suppress the tumor.

Pregnant women used thalidomide to prevent morning sickness in the 1950s. Doctors didn't know at the time that the drug could suppress the growth of new blood vessels. These women gave birth to limbless children, which was a terrible thing. In retrospect, it was discovered that the drug inhibited the development and growth of blood vessels in the fetuses of these women. The scandal led to criminal prosecutions and millions of dollars in compensation. The drug was given to adults with metastasizing cancer to stop the natural development of blood vessels in adults. The results of the trial were not conclusive, so thalidomide treatment was stopped.

According to my experience, a radiologist interprets the bone scan. The results of the exam are sent to patients by the institute that performs the bone scan. I was not happy with the slow process. There was an increasing urgency to find out what was happening inside of my body. To get the best results, I used my persuasive skills to convince the secretary of the bone scan office. I begged the secretary to decipher it as quickly as possible. I told her I would pick it up, rather than waiting for it to arrive in the mail. She promised the results would be available within four days. Uneasy, I took the number of the office and walked out.

I was to receive my bloodwork results from 11 days earlier on Thursday the day after. To review the results with Dr. Solan, I made an appointment in advance. I printed the results from my computer station and found that they were all within normal limits, except for Alkaline Phosphatase. The norm is between 34-104. I had 400. The result sheet was with me as I entered the doctor's room. I sat beside him with my usual aloofness. He looked at the results with satisfaction written across it until he found the abnormal result. As he looked at the results with a satisfied expression, he said, "Ohhhh, so it's not making it up!" I was stunned by how naive I had been over the past year. I kept going back to him, complaining about my health deteriorating. He had the audacity of thinking I was making it up.

I tried to be businesslike. He explained that it was an enzyme related the bone and liver. I asked him about what that meant. He explained that I needed to test for iso-enzyme alkalinephosphatase to find out. I was given a referral and sent home. I realized that I could not take the test because it was Thursday night. I would need to wait ten days to see the results. That would be two weeks. With the rapid deterioration in my body, I was unable to withstand two weeks. I took matters into my own hands. I felt a sense of urgency and began to act quickly. I called my doctor and asked him to reduce the time it took for me to get the results. I was impatient and he replied that he didn't know of any way. I knew I was going to get nowhere with him so I made inquiries that led to me turning to the Haifa Hospital information center. A nurse friend suggested I could take the test quickly.

— ◊ —

We drove to Sarona on Saturday for a visit with the family. I felt horrible. My whole body hurt. I couldn't walk or climb stairs. I tried to pretend business as usual, but with no success.

We sat down at Arieh's house for the evening. He asked me about my limping. I said that I was not in good health. Although I didn't know what it was, I knew that something was wrong with my body. He asked me more. It was hard for me to explain to him the exact problem. Although he tried to console me by saying that it was a temporary thing or what people might say in these situations, deep down I knew that I was in a very bad place.

After a difficult Saturday, I managed to gather myself and schedule an urgent appointment at Haifa Hospital to take the test. I completed the test the same day and received the results by noon. The urgent test cost me 57 shekels (15). Angrily, I called Nahariya's health clinic and requested that they pay for the test. They said it was against regulations and that I had done the test on my own initiative. They also stated that only oncological patients are eligible for funding these tests. I replied, "Listen, although I don't know if my cancer is, I know that I must take this test immediately."

Retrospectively, I can see that after I told the woman I spoke to that I was "oncological", she informed me that the clinic would reimburse my expenses.

The Institute of Nuclear Medicine woman promised me that the results of the bone scan would be available by Sunday. I called her on Sunday to ask for assistance. I was told by the person answering the phone that she had left and that results would not be available that day. I decided to take care of my business and go to the hospital. After insisting that I get the results immediately, I was called to the radioologist's office. He, with a serious expression, informed me that there were "absorptions" in my bones. I asked him about what this meant. He explained that it could be due to previous fractures, fissures or bone disorders like Paget's disease.

Paget's disease is a bone-related chronic condition that causes bone pain. Paget patients might fracture their bones more easily due to the damage they have suffered. A bone scan of a Paget patient shows absorptions similar to those that result from bone metastases caused by cancer.

The radiologist asked me if it was cancer. In a way that could have been interpreted in any direction, he nodded and said in a weak voice yes, it could be. It's amazing how a doctor who deals with diagnosing and treating cancer can not even utter the words "cancer" from his mouth. If I had not asked him, he wouldn't have suggested that cancer could be the cause of the absorptions. My mother, a former cancer patient, couldn't even spell the name. It was simply a tumor, as she said to the doctor. He said, "You have tumor.".

We all agreed that the radiologist would send Dr. Solan the results.

Over the years, I returned to the bone scan institute several times for checkups. He would stare at me with wonderment every time, as though I were an alien from another world. Does it just feel subjectively that my days as patient are over? I don't know. However, I'm still happy to "disapoint" him every time.

The results of the Haifa Hospital test in the morning and the bone scan gave me a strange sense of accomplishment. I beat the system. It took me one day to accomplish what was supposed to take two weeks. But I realized I was in serious trouble.

The next day, Dr. Solan saw me and informed me that I was being hospitalized. The same doctor who had just denied any possibility of me being sick and believed I was making it up, told me that he was going to send me to hospital.

Without the bone scan results that I had received without his knowledge and assistance, he wouldn't have the information to make this decision. Ironically, I didn't need the isoenzyme for alkalinephosphatase test that he had instructed me to take. This was something I worked so hard to get. I asked him if he knew if I had ever been diagnosed with cancer.

Rivka was informed at home that I was in hospital. Surprised, she was. She was shocked. We are generally a calm family who handle situations with a non-panicking, matter-of-fact manner. We also notified our children. We tried to maintain a calm atmosphere and pretend that it was nothing important. Apart from the fear of the unknown, I felt a strange sense of relief. It was because I was entrusting my "project" to professional entities, and was taking the burden off my shoulders.

It was like being on reserve. You will need a towel, clothes, toiletry bags, and clothing. Ilana, our neighbor and good friend, visited us to check in and give an update. We sat down together and drank coffee, laughing, as if we were releasing tension. In a matter of days, I realized that I had a reserve duty draft. I faxed my unit asking for an exemption from duty because of medical reasons. We drove to the hospital at nine o'clock that evening to confirm my anxious feelings.

CHAPTER THREE

HOSPITALIZATION

Late January 2002

I was referred to the hospital's emergency room. It was noisy and crowded, despite the fact that it was late. The work ethic of the chief doctor impressed me. Under the pressure of patients and their attendants, she managed a tight ship and made informed decisions about the best treatment for each patient based on the information she had. Everything went smoothly. Rivka was waiting outside in hopelessness when I suggested that she return home. With a sense of relief, she accepted my suggestion. We parted with love.

After reviewing my medical file, the emergency room staff decided to place me in the internal hospital ward. I was surprised, even though I knew that it would happen. I was not hospitalized or have ever fallen seriously ill, but suddenly became a patient on the internal ward. A nurse made me push myself in a wheelchair to the ward, as if this were not enough. From that point on, I was a dependent patient and needed to be taken to the ward.

Transport services are provided from one place to another.

In the ward, there is a bed waiting for me with sheets and pajamas. I fall asleep, exhausted from the day's trials and tribulations. I am grateful for some restful sleep to help me forget about the difficult journey I've taken. After I lay my head down on the pillow, and started to drift into sleep, the lights in my bedroom turned on and a young, blonde, female doctor came in to check me out. She was probably a Russian immigrant, judging by her accent. This was a pleasant surprise in the midst of all the chaos. She took some blood from me, and then she left. I was ready to go to sleep again but a nurse came to check my blood pressure and temperature. I pulled the covers up again after the nurse examination was over. I hoped that I wouldn't be interrupted any more and fell asleep until the next morning.

The hospital's routine was established and maintained. Breakfast was served at eight in the morning. After cleaning the room, a nurse came to check my temperature, pulse and blood pressure. After the examinations were over, the doctor's visit became a ritual. The chief doctor in charge led the band, followed closely by the rest of the junior doctors, or the chicks. The ward head stopped at the bed of the patient, with the chief doctor in charge at his feet and the junior doctors where they could. This arrangement - the patient on his bed, the medical staff around him - prompted a serious professional discussion about his condition.

Even though I did not understand the medical terminology, I was able to deduce from the doctors body language and expressions that I was in serious condition. Every concern or eyebrow raised was reflected in the test results. These all led to a more worrying picture of my health, but I felt hopeful that things would turn out for the best. I was otherwise healthy so it wasn't that bad.

After my first visit to the doctor, I had to go through a series general tests, including blood and urine. Slowly, I began to settle into hospital life. My cell phone allowed me to stay in constant contact with Rivka and other people. Many people heard about my hospitalization and began to visit. Rivka gave me a transistor radio. Rivka brought me a book and my visitors brought another. I was able to read a lot.

I moved from the middle to the closest bed to the window and rearranged my room. I made friends with a few patients and met some of their families. We shared meals together, and we spent our time discussing politics and getting to know one another. In the ward's dining hall, we formed a sort of parliament. We spent hours talking and sharing jokes. It was as if we were all on vacation. The atmosphere was one of camaraderie, ease and camaraderie. I developed good relationships with the nurses and doctors, which would be invaluable later.

I walked through the hallways of the hospital ward, until I came to the doctors' offices. I noticed the bulletin board and the announcement by the hospital assistant director directing doctors not to take blood samples from patients - especially the more costly tests as the budget for the year was almost exhausted. It was interesting to me, considering that blood tests are the main indicator of a patient's health. Without running tests, how could they diagnose? It was like taking away a carpenter's measuring tape and telling him to do without it for the remainder of the year. It turns out that hospitals are managed just like any other business. The budget is the most important. The patients? They are the last.

Two days passed. Two days passed. I was unable to understand why it happened, and he didn't bother to explain to me.

The exam was short and the doctor seemed happy, as if finding what he was looking.

Digital rectal examination (DRE) is the name of the examination performed by the doctor. The purpose of this examination is to examine the prostate gland for changes. A patient might have prostate cancer if there are lumps in his prostate gland. The patient must lie on his back, fetal, for this examination. The doctor inserts his gloved fingers and carefully examines the prostate gland. This is one of the few exams that doctors can use to get a clear picture about a patient's health.

I was sent for a CT scan the next day. This scan scans various parts of the body with multiple X-rays, and digitally transforms them into a clear picture.

The doctor who was in charge of my ward was an impressive woman called Dr. A. She was a very nice person and I felt that I could help her understand what was going on. After the CT results were in, she called me to come see her. Rivka was asked to come along, as I warned her we were about to experience the shock of our lifetimes. Rivka kept reminding me that I was reacting too much and refused to believe her prediction.

When we arrived at the doctor's, she explained to us that I had prostate cancer and metastases in my bones. The treatment for this type is quite simple and one can cope with it for years, she said. She recommended that I immediately begin hormonal treatment and she scheduled an appointment to see Dr. Bassam. A biopsy of the prostate gland is required to confirm diagnosis and assess severity.

We both walked out weeping. I was stunned. I was dumbstruck?
I was diagnosed with cancer and moved into a new phase of my life.

It was difficult to take in such bad news. It was always someone else's disease, and I became emotional whenever I heard about someone close to me being diagnosed with cancer. These feelings included sadness, pity and the realization that this person might soon die. It was never in my mind that I could get cancer. In my subconscious, I'm still healthy to this day.

My GP, Dr. Solan was the cause of my anger. He failed to diagnose my illness on time and thought I was lying. It never occurred to me to speed up the testing. Most importantly, though, I was angry at him for allowing me to believe that I was healthy, numbing all my instincts, and allowing me this present state.

— ◊ —

We knew that we needed to inform the family. Rivka debated the best time and method to inform her parents. She was on vacation in the Dead Sea, and was afraid to tell her parents over the telephone. I advised her to inform them because they could hear it from another person, which would be unpleasant. Rivka called them as well as other family members. Dror, my partner at the dairy farm, was also informed that evening.

Rivka decided to tell the children.

Amir was thirteen years old when she broke the news to him while driving him to Nahariya train station after a soccer practice. He was a member of the youth soccer team, and he traveled three times per week to practice in Haifa. He was stunned, broke down, and began asking practical questions in his own unique way. What was my remaining time? Is there any chance of recovery?

The topic was not new to him, as he knew a friend who had lost his father to terminal cancer just a few months before. His grandmother, his mother, had also died from terminal cancer. This added to his anxiety. Rivka and Amir met me at the hospital. I will never forget what transpired there. Amir approached me palely to confirm the information he received from Rivka. Did it get diagnosed in time? Did I die? So on. I tried to be calm and as reassuring as possible, sometimes even going so far as to fabricate reality. It wasn't fair or logical for me to tell him all the truth, so I kept some facts to myself. I hugged him, explained the facts to him, and told him that I was likely to recover from my illness.

Orr, our oldest son, was to return from a navigation program, where he was a counselor. Rivka informed him of the news when he returned. He was shocked, not surprising. He was confused and lost, not knowing what questions to ask or how to respond. He began to get more information and gradually got over the initial shock. He knows my delicate condition, but he doesn't ask too many questions. He knows enough for us both to know what he knows. I once heard him tell me that he gets all his information about me from our conversations. I asked him if there was any missing information. He said no but I tried to update him as much as I could. It strengthened our relationship and brought us closer together.

Our daughter Bat-El was on a short trip. Rivka let Bat-El enjoy the trip and told her when she returned.

The subject of my illness is still a topic that comes up in family conversations, just like any other topic. The children ask technical questions about the treatment, type of cancer, and medication. None of these questions concern my chances of survival or my expected lifespan.

My reserve unit secretary called me to inquire why I had not shown up for duty. A draft notice that I had prepared coincided with my third day in hospital was sent to me. I informed her that I had a medical issue and asked Ami to contact me. Ami was my commander and a lieutenant colonel, as well as a fellow engineer. Our friendship was very close and lasted a long time. The commander of the reserves office called me the next day and asked me the same question. I answered the same as the day before, asking Ami to contact me. Ami called me on the third day. Ami called me on the third day. I informed him that I was at the hospital with cancer. I was stunned and lost for words. He finally said something along the lines of "Be well" and then hung up. A few months later, I received an exempt certificate which exempted myself from any further duty. It did not contain any personal information.

A recurring dream in which I was called to duty despite my illness was a constant experience. Nobody knew I was sick and they refused to release me from reserve duty.

I found the service physically demanding. I was forced into service, even though I was entitled to full exemption from reserve duty. Yet, despite this and against my will, it was still a constant battle to stay on duty. I promised myself that I would bring my medical documentation with me the next time I served and refused to continue serving.

Ami has never called me again over the years.

He was a random person I met three years after my initial hospital stay. He wanted to know how I was doing. I replied with anger and a sour tone of voice "What happened? "Why do you care so much about my performance suddenly? It was all you cared about for the past three years and now it's your turn to ask." He looked embarrassed. His companion, however, didn't understand and tried to get answers from him. I watched as they left and read their body language, trying to understand what he was trying to tell her.

— ◊ —

The hormonal treatment was initiated immediately. This treatment is recommended for patients with prostate cancer who have had their disease spread to other parts of the body. The small Casodex pill is taken daily with Zoladex injection into the stomach every three months. Dr. A was kind and tried to get me the Casodex tablets that day. Each was 150 mg and I required 50 mg. They broke the pill with a special device and gave me one third every time. It happened twice that the nurse forgot about breaking it and gave me a whole pill. I was careful and ordered her to break it. This was another warning sign. I thought to myself, "Hail, Pay Attention!" As you know, the medical profession is not immune to making mistakes. Staff work in shifts so it is possible that not all instructions are given. You must ensure that they don't fail you again. Although I don't know what I would have done if I took the full 150-milligram dose, it is certain that it would have not been good for my health.

I realized in retrospect that 150mg of intensive, prolonged treatment is not recommended for severe cases. It can cause hormonal side effects such as breast enlargement. This would have been a terrible thing to do.

To develop prostate cancer, the body must have enough testosterone. Medical professionals have known this for many years. The cancer will dissipate if it is devoid of testosterone. This is the essence hormonal treatment. This process can be compared to starving a tree of water. It would then naturally become dehydrated.

Casodex pills block the receptors within the cells of the body, so that testosterone can't penetrate the cells. This makes it impossible for cancer cells to grow.

The Zoladex shot was the second medication. The substance is administered into the stomach using a syringe that is as thick as a match, or a toothpick. This signals the brain to stop the production of testosterone. A single dose lasts twelve weeks.

Hormonal treatment has side effects that can be unpleasant. It only works for a short time. The rule of thumb is that hormone treatment has a shorter effect on cancers that are more severe.

As I said, I was referred to Dr. Bassam as an oncologist. He is the head of the hospital's outpatient oncology ward and is well-known in the field. Rivka and I met him the next day. We were supposed to meet Dr. Bassam but Dr. Rassan, a different doctor, welcomed us and said that he would become my oncologist. It was strange to imagine meeting Dr. Bassam, only to find out that I was being treated by another doctor with all the implications.

Dr. Rassan reviewed my medical records and performed a third rectal exam on me. (I was also examined and examined by a senior physician who, after pushing his finger up my anus, claimed that he had also checked my father for prostate cancer. Fortunately, it was not aggressive.

I felt terrible. My stomach was churned repeatedly. This invasive examination was not only uncomfortable, but it also had a humiliating aspect, a near-rape. If you don't know what I mean, it wasn't exactly my cup of tea.

I was confirmed by my doctor that hormonal therapy was appropriate for me. We asked many questions, and he said that side effects of the treatment included a decrease in sexual desire as well as hot flashes. We agreed that if this was the price of survival, we would endure it. We both left him feeling relieved and almost euphoric that everything was under control.

Dr. A explained that I needed to have a biopsy of my prostate gland. She also said that there was no room in the operating room for me on Thursday. Thursday, November 1, 2001, arrived and the slot I had been assigned was not available. I felt like a hitchhiker waiting in the operating room for a slot that would allow me to undergo the procedure. I complained to Dr. A. She explained that operating rooms are booked well in advance, and that even though I was on the wait list, there had been no openings. I was admitted to hospital for the remainder of the week. On Monday, a slot opened up and I had to undergo this painful procedure. The hospital biopsy was unsuccessful. I will return to this issue later.

A prostate biopsy is a surgical procedure that involves the removal of some cells from the prostate gland in order to perform a microscopic examination. The samples are examined to determine if the cells of the prostate gland that were removed are cancerous. The doctor inserts a sonogram into the patient's rectum to view the prostate gland. This device uses a needle with a special tip that can be used to penetrate the large intestinal wall and into the prostate gland. It also allows for the collection of cells to be microscopically examined. The biopsy leaves blood traces in the urine of the patient for several days. In rare cases, it might cause an infection.

A prostate biopsy should include at least six (or more) samples. This allows for a complete mapping of the prostate gland.

— ◊ —

Al and Oren, Mitzpe Hila friends, were among my visitors. Oren had been diagnosed with skin cancer in her past and was recently treated with chemotherapy and surgery. She seemed to be fully recovered. She is now completely healthy and the couple even had a baby after her recovery. They were both experienced and kind enough to send me numerous articles about prostate cancer. They also stressed the importance of self-knowledge when making important decisions. I was determined to learn everything about my situation. I read all of the articles and couldn't stop reading them. It was difficult to comprehend what I was reading at first. The material was written in English and had many terms that I was unfamiliar with. But I quickly came to some realizations that were like heavy rock.

First, patients with a two-year life expectancy are eligible for hormonal treatment.

Second, hormonal treatment for patients like me only works for nine months on average. After that time it ceases to be effective and the cancer returns. Numerous times, I asked doctors what to do if the hormonal treatment had stopped working. I was told that second-line protocols were available, but this seemed vague to me. There was no other treatment.

A third truth is that a metastatic cancer such as mine is incurable. I would remain a cancer patient until my death. Since my cancer will likely end my life, the goal of all medications and treatments was to buy me time. It was hard for me to accept the fact that I had no chance of recovery. I was the eternally healthy and at the same time a terminal patient.

It was difficult to accept such truths. I was plagued by the darkest thoughts. It is impossible to fully comprehend what it means without having experienced it.

These thoughts were triggered by me wondering what I would do to my children, who hadn't yet turned into adults. What if Amir doesn't make it? My sweet, young boy. What if they don't marry me in a few years? As I struggled to comprehend the meaning of an ending, I was plagued by terrible thoughts. I was underground as a corpse and contemplated many other morbid things. I tried to keep my composure, and not allow anyone to see what was going on in my head.

After my initial week in hospital, and the spread of the news about my illness, a large number of relatives, friends, and visitors began to arrive. Yaron, the dairy's head of production and a trusted friend, came to visit me one evening. He asked me, with sincere concern, "What will happen?" I tried my best to calm him down and promised that I would make it through, even though I wasn't sure if it was true. I was greatly encouraged by this sudden attention and genuine concern for my future. I was distracted by the number of people who came to see me, and my current state. Despite my current condition, I was able to display a cheerfulness that I could not explain.

During family visits, a coalition was formed which pressured me to leave Nahariya's hospital and move to another, more serious hospital. Rivka and I were informed by the concerned group that this hospital was a provincial one. A serious hospital would have a more skilled staff, better equipment, and better overall conditions. I did not automatically accept this assumption, nor did I have enough information to make any adjustments. Based on my engineering experience and in complete alignment with my personality, I made the following three important decisions about my conduct starting at that point:

First, I would only make decisions about me that are in my best judgment. I wouldn't allow anyone to force me to go from one expert to another like a puppet, without my consent or permission.

Second, I would base all future decisions on knowledge and understanding. I would never turn to pseudo-dietitians, mystics, or other miracle-makers or wizards--with or with out credentials. I later resorted to seeing a few "mystics" despite this decision.

Third, Rivka and I agreed to a policy that my medical information would be made public. I believed and still believe that concealing the illness is a waste. It was already widely known and it would be impossible to conceal the fact. Rivka and me had to focus our energy on the task at hand. We decided not to share details about my life expectancy and the type of treatment that I was receiving. I was clear that I didn't want to share the details of my treatments or their side effects with anyone but my family. I also did not want people to wonder how long I had left.

I resolved to do everything in my power and not compromise my health. I was prepared for any aggressive treatment that might affect my quality of life, so long as I could keep living.

— ◊ —

My older brother Arieh was the closest to me. He had offered to help in any way possible. He and Dina visited me almost every day, despite the pressure of work. Arieh would call me a few times per day to update me when they weren't there. Arieh is an owner of horse stables and a member in good standing of a horseback riding club. This group includes employees and freelancers from all walks of life, including farmers, Arabs, and the rich. The group rode throughout the country together. Arieh was able to meet many interesting people along the way, including Dr. Ruthie, a pediatrician and her husband Daniel. They had briefly met me on Saturday, the day before I was admitted to hospital. We also bumped into one another at Arieh's stables. In retrospect I realized that Ruthie noticed me limping and alerted my brother.

You might be wondering why I am telling you this. It may seem irrelevant except that Arieh called me to tell me that Ruthie had offered to take my case and help me in any way she could. Arieh sought my permission to make this intriguing offer. Since I was confused and helpless at the time, it seemed like a great idea. All the advice I received only made my confusion worse. Should I leave the hospital? See this doctor or that mystic? Eat wheat grass. It is clear that I received the best advice from a professional to help me navigate this chaos and focus on the essence.

Ruthie had one thing on her to-do list: consult Rabbi Fhurrer. Fhurrer is a single-man organization that knows how to match patients with appropriate treatment and the right medical establishment, both in Israel or abroad. Rabbi Fhurrer, a world-renowned expert in this field, has been awarded the Israel Prize. Arieh, Dina and Ruthie arrived at the hospital Saturday night to obtain my medical file to give to Rabbi Fhurrer. The doctor in charge, the pretty blonde who examined me the first night, refused to allow us to photocopy my file but he did agree to read it aloud. Ruthie took down the details that the doctor read. Most of these I didn't understand back then. Ruthie filled in any gaps and clarified what I didn't understand. This didn't add to my optimism.

They had already scheduled an appointment for me with Rabbi Fhurrer on the next day. It can take a while to make an appointment with him. But Irit, my brother Izhar, was able to get it done quicker. She is a Channel 2 director and uses her connections to assist us in bureaucratic matters.

The meeting was scheduled for Sunday, November 4th at 8 p.m. at the house of the rabbi. I was still in hospital. The "team" believed that the meeting was scheduled for eight in the morning. The rabbi wasn't at home when they arrived. He was in another location and had a very strict schedule. He was able to meet them and recommended that I have the entire treatment in Israel. He also mentioned a few well-respected doctors, including Dr. Avivit Neumann.

On Monday the following day, a slot was finally available at the hospital for my prostate biopsies. Because of the volume of work in the operating room, they didn't notify me beforehand about the exact time. They simply stated that there was a good possibility it would happen that day. Their attitude made me feel somewhat embarrassed. Did they think I was a second-class patient and would only treat me if another operation was cancelled? Even worse, I was forced to stay in the hospital for five consecutive days to undergo that bizarre biopsy. I was told by someone that the hospital is paid by the clinics for the time patients spend there. It is therefore in the hospital's best interest to keep patients there as long as possible. Otherwise, they may have to reduce their medical staff. The ward was only half full, to be honest. This could have been the cause. Dr. A was able to understand my disappointment and apologize.

A nurse brought a hospital bed with a gown and asked me to put it on and lay down. He rolled me up on the bed, and I was able to climb on it. This is the area where all patients are "parked" side-by-side, waiting for their operation, and others in recovery. A majority of patients were accompanied at least one family member. I was the only one. Since the procedure was simple and quick, I didn't need to have a relative. Nonetheless, I felt lonely. It brought back memories of the loneliness I felt when family members visited my army base, but no one came to see me. It wasn't part of our family tradition. My parents did not visit me in the military or at Acre's naval officers' boarding school. My parents were hardworking and didn't have a car. I, for my part, always claimed it was unnecessary. My home didn't understand the "bourgeois" practice of visiting children on weekends or holidays. They didn't want it on their agenda. We make every effort to visit our children on Saturdays, regardless of whether they are in the military or elsewhere--as much and as often as possible, as long as we get their approval.

The atmosphere in the operating room was relaxed and ethereal. Some staff were getting ready for bed, and I could see from their conversations that it was the end of the day. It felt like they were hurrying to get the last patients.

After waiting in the parking lot for the operating room, the anesthesiologist approached and asked me, "How would you like to do it?".

He replied, "You can do this without anesthesia. But you should use an anesthetic cream that numbs the sensation or with a short-term general or local anesthesia.".

I spoke with him and determined that a biopsy would be performed under a brief-acting general anesthesia. The surgeon arrived shortly after and introduced himself to me. I asked how many samples he would take from my prostate. He replied, "One sample will suffice." His answer was amazing to me. His answer was a surprise to me. I'd read in articles that it takes at least six samples to map the spread of prostate cancer. It was possible to randomly take a sample from an area free of cancer cells. This would mean that the result would be negative, even though the patient might be very sick. He just shrugged off my doubts. I felt very disappointed by his unprofessional attitude and condescending manner. Although I realize I should not have performed the biopsy, I was weak and unable to resist the temptation. I fell asleep quickly after the anesthesiologist put a mask on my face.

About fifteen minutes later, I awoke up in the parking lot near the operating rooms with a mild needling sensation in both my buttocks. I was soon back on the ward. There was blood in my urine at night but this was normal. Dr. A informed me that I would be going home the next day. As soon as the biopsy results were in, she promised to keep me informed by phone.

Rivka came to assist me in the dismissal process. Before the dismissal, Rivka had requested all X-rays of my body and other medical information to get further opinions. The doctors had to write a dismissal letter that detailed my medical condition and provided further instructions for treatment. A Russian doctor wrote the letter, making numerous spelling errors and forgetting to give instructions for the injections I would need every three months. I brought it to his attention and he signed it.

We didn't understand much of the letter as we read it. We did learn that my prostate carcinoma had spread to my spine and shoulder bones.

Carcinoma is a form of cancer that spreads from epithelial tissue, which lines the skin and internal organs. It can also metastasize to other parts of the body.

The PSA test was part of the bloodwork that they had done on me. My PSA was 530 the day I arrived at hospital. It rose to 564 the next day. I was not informed of this information during my week-long hospital stay.

PSA (prostate-specific antigen) is a protein that is released by the prostate into blood. In 1980, the correlation between high blood levels of this protein and prostate cancer was established. This revolutionized early detection of the disease. In healthy individuals, the value is typically less than 4. The units in which protein is measured are from nanogram to milliliter. This means that one over a billionth to a thousandth of liters of blood can be measured in these units. If the value is greater than 4, it is possible that the patient has prostate cancer. Any value above 500 is considered extremely high and may indicate a widespread spread of the disease.

The PSA doubling rate or PSADT is an important indicator in this regard. This index shows the disease's spread rate. If a patient has a PSA 10, and then a year later has a PSA 20, his PSADT is one.

My PSA measurement in hospital showed that I had a PSADT of 12 days. My PSA would have risen to over 1,000 without the hormonal treatment that I received in hospital. These PSA levels are rare in patients. It's scary as hell.

A metastasized prostate tumor is defined by how severe it has spread. They were spread widely, which was why I had so many.

The hospital discharge process took several hours. We said goodbye to Dr. A and the head of the ward, as well the staff who looked after me. Everyone supported us and wished us health and a long life. I said farewell to other patients as I walked out of the hospital in my regular clothes into a spring day. I felt a pleasant feeling of freedom. We drove to Nahariya for a meal and to celebrate this happy-sad occasion.

Rivka drove unlike in olden days, while I, the patient, sat on the passenger's side.

CHAPTER FOUR

A NEW ROUTINE:
COMING HOME AS A CANCER PHILIPPIENT

Early February 2002

We finally arrived home. I was pacing back and forth, uncontrollably. I was unsure how to act in this new environment. I felt uncomfortable in my own skin. I'm sick! Do I need to stay in bed? Or should I get up and move around so I can act normally?

I decided to call a few people. I called my dad and informed him that I was back. I called my brother Arieh and Dror, my partner, as well as some friends. Deep down, I felt the need to be surrounded as much as possible because those visits would lift both my spirits and my sore body.

My first night in bed was a strange one. It took me a while to adjust to Rivka's body and the way she cared for me. Even in the most difficult moments, she was able to radiate warmth & love. This was also evident in the next nights. Rivka put her body against mine, as hard as she could, and as long as I let her. Due to my pain, the physical contact was difficult for me at times. Every movement in my posture caused me pain. Sometimes I had to push her away so that she could change into a position that was less painful. This intimacy made me feel very comfortable.

The next day I took my time getting up from bed. I didn't have anything to do so I took my time eating breakfast and decided to head to the dairy. I arrived at work before noon and was again confused about what to do next. What was my exact role in the company? It was impossible for me to go back to the way I used to work. Office work was the only thing that I could do. I still felt lousy. Although the hormonal treatment was not yet fully in place, the physical problems I faced before being admitted remained the same. My shaky emotional state made it worse. Dror's great wisdom told me, casually, that "Just do what it takes." This key phrase was the one that helped me get further along the path. Dror may not have realized how important it was to me or how deeply I absorbed his words. According to how I felt, we agreed that I would arrive at work at eight o'clock in the morning and remain there until I was tired. He was responsible for the dairy business, as well as his other agricultural activities such the goat herd and orchards. Dror was also the chairperson of his agricultural society, where he spent a lot time. I was aware of the pressure Dror was under and knew that the dairy would bear the brunt.

At home, we set up a "war room". We had to quickly learn about all the topics in our lives, get as much information as we could, and make informed decisions. It was important that I receive the best possible treatment, and possibly even recover from the worst.

Four chiefs manned the war room, each with a specific area of responsibility:
Rivka was the chief. Her responsibility was to find top doctors in the field and consult them. She also took care of all the guests who came to her home. Arieh, my older brother and second chief, was responsible for coordinating all

the entities and making sure I was able to keep my head above water. He dedicated to me a song that brought me to tears and touched my heart as part of his job. Barbara J. wrote the song "The Sun will Shine on You Again". Hall sums up my hope for overcoming hardship, even though it seemed almost impossible at the time. The song describes a time when you can overcome your troubles. You and the sun have much in common, and you'll both shine no matter what.

Dear Dr. Ruthie - who, as I said, took me on as an individual case while contacting various medical experts - was the third chief.

Together, my younger brother Izhar (and his partner Irit) were the fourth chief. They set out to collect information and connect with people outside the country who could assist. They were extremely efficient. Irit's connections were a great help.

I was proud of my family for their non-stop activity. It was an amazing enlistment, full of people who wanted to help me. Each time we discussed the issue, I would become teary-eyed or overcome with emotion.

Our plan was gradually developed. I used the solid principles that I had established for myself to only approach experts and not let anyone else make the decision for me. We decided to consult Dr.

Vaida was taken from a Jerusalem hospital, while Dr. Avivit Neumann was taken from a Tel Aviv hospital.

Dr. A called me while I was still awake, beginning with "I have bad news" and I thought I was about to faint. I thought she was going tell me I was about dying the next day. When I asked her about what had happened, my voice was shaking. The biopsy had failed, she said. I breathed a sigh of relief and replied, "No big deal. I thought it was worse." I then thought that I had a negative feeling about the biopsy from the beginning and that my gut feelings were correct every time. I realized that I had to listen to my intuitions and trust my gut more. Although she scheduled another biopsy at the hospital for me, I knew that I didn't intend to do it there again.

Rivka was recommended by friends to a doctor who performed biopsies at the Tel Aviv healthcare clinic. We made an appointment for the 5th of November at 3:00pm. Following the clinic's instructions I performed an enema before I went. Rivka helped me and I followed the instructions on my kit. It was horrible. It was so horrible?

Rivka and me left for Tel Aviv. It was a great help to have someone to talk to during those difficult days. Because of my situation, my emotional state was affected and I needed to have close friends, especially since I was moving into the unknown. We had made contact with the doctor and were able to quickly find ourselves in a small darkened room measuring ten meters square. There was equipment along the walls and a hospital bed. The room was occupied by the doctor and his assistant. I was asked by the doctor to climb onto the bed and take off my pants. Then, he instructed me to lie on one side in fetal position. I did what he asked me to do. He put a round instrument in my anus. This was most likely the sonogram camera's head that recorded the prostate during the biopsy. The assistant was busy looking at the screen on the computer and reviewing the images of the prostate. There was a clicking sound that indicated that the spring was moving. The spring was released and a pincher was used to extract the first gland sample. It was as if someone was ripping apart my flesh. Soon thereafter, another cocking and another pinching were heard. They became more resistant to the pinches the more they were fired. My body began to contract involuntarily as soon as I felt the pinches. The doctor asked me to stop. After the fifth pinch, he said "Okay," and I shouted at him to stop. He replied, "Okay," and fired the pincher six more times. Then he pulled out the device and said, "That's it." I felt like I was going into a coma. After a while, I sat down on the bed and got dressed. Then, I walked to the waiting room lit by the lights. Rivka, who was outside waiting for me, asked, "Why are you so pale?" I didn't know what kind of torture I'd just endured in the room. I sat on the bench of the clinic until I felt better, then we set off. We decided to have fun and go out. We met a friend and neighbor from Sarona at the mall. We talked for a while. We didn't mention my illness, although it was over our heads. As if evaluating my condition, I felt our friend stare at me back as we parted.

After eating at the mall, we went to the cinema. Under the Sand is a French film about a woman who lost her husband at sea. He was gone, but she couldn't accept it. She kept believing in him and felt as if he were right beside her. I wondered if the movie had foreshadowed our future.

— ◊ —

We received an answer from the clinic a few days later. It was clear and quite grim that the diagnosis was made. My diagnosis was that I had prostate cancer. My Gleason score of 8 and my PSA above 500 indicated that the cancer was severe. Additionally, I had metastases all the way up to my shoulders as well as two small metastases that were located in my lung.

Gleason scores are a measure of the aggressiveness of prostate carcinoma. This is done by microscopic examinations of prostate tissue taken during biopsy. Gleason 10 represents the most aggressive and highest grade. Gleason scores, along with PSA levels and DRE results, help determine treatment options and other tests that will be needed before a treatment can be chosen.

— ◊ —

The average wait time to see Professor Niv at the Haifa hospital was one to two months. Our relative, Orna, was a dear woman who worked as a head nurse on the hospital's urological ward. She had helped my father with some urological issues he had had in the past. Her opinion was sought by my father, who asked her for her advice. She had also recommended Professor Niv to him, whom we have heard nothing but good things about from a few other sources. A week later, I was released from the hospital and I went to his clinic in Haifa, accompanied by Rivka, my loyal support. After reviewing my medical records, he assured us that the treatment that I was receiving was appropriate and that I would be okay. We found him condescending and reluctant to share any information, but he answered all our questions quickly. We tried to get more information from him but he only said that it was the right treatment and everything would be okay. We parted ways with mixed feelings. He promised me that I would be fine, but we didn't gain any insight.

We drove to Jerusalem to meet Dr. Vaida a few days later. As part of Hadassah Hospital's private medical services, he sees patients. Eight years ago, I had brought my mother's medical records to the same place, hoping to find a treatment. It was a disappointing experience. The expert then confirmed the horrible prognosis she had received at Tiberias Hospital, which was that her condition was terminal and lethal. She could not be helped by any medical tools other than narcotic painkillers.

The doctor was more sympathetic than the previous expert and was very down-to-earth. We were welcomed warmly by the doctor who explained from the beginning that doctors like all human beings have limited knowledge and should not be relied upon too much. This was, in retrospect, the most valuable insight that I gained during that meeting. It would prove to be very useful later. He was supportive of the treatment I received and encouraged us to be positive. We were so impressed by the man that we made the decision to make him my supervisor for Nahariya's treatment. Rivka was completely in love with him and I was concerned that she would want to stay around longer. Fortunately, she is shy. He opened a line of communication with us and allowed us to reach out to him for any problems that may arise. These consultants require that you see them at least once and pay them $200. Then they will treat your as a member of their hospital ward. This means that two hundred dollars will get you into their ward.

We left Dr. Vaida feeling optimistic and happy as we headed to Izhar, our brother. Irit and Irit had been there for me since I was sick. They also recruited all the help they could. We were due to meet Shmulik, a religious Jew who helps patients connect with those who can help them.

Shmulik was a friend we met at Izhar's home. Shmulik is one such religious person. Izhar had sent him a copy my medical file before he arrived, so he knew the details. He shared stories about terminal patients who couldn't find answers in Israel's medical system and were sent to the United States for treatment. There, innovative treatments helped them recover and get a second chance. He provided my medical information to several medical institutions in the United States, with whom he had connections. They sent him information about their trials for prostate cancer.

He suggested that we immediately check out the possibility of me participating in one of these trials, so that we could be prepared to leave when the hormonal treatment stops working. After the initial feeling of optimism, I was confronted with the harsh reality that the hormonal treatment had only temporary benefits and that I was on borrowed time. We agreed to his suggestion. We decided to keep going and seek out experts so we wouldn't waste time or make hasty choices.

Dr. Ruthie made an appointment with Dr. Avivit Neumann at the hospital near Tel Aviv, on Friday, November 16, 2001. Dr. Avivit Neumann was visiting New York City for a conference at the time and she agreed to meet us the next day. She is a respected medical professional and is very dedicated to her patients. Rivka and me picked up Dr. Ruthie at home while we were on our way. Avivit reviewed my medical file. She almost involuntarily said, "Eh...your outlook is pretty grim." But she then realized her mistake and responded, "It'll be fine." We will do what it takes.

Prognosis, which means "forecast" Greek, refers to a doctor's prediction about the course of a patient's illness and the chances of his recovery. This term can also be used in non-medical contexts such as the business world. Both the doctor and the patient benefit from knowing the prognosis. Everyone can make an informed decision about whether or not to seek medical treatment. A prognosis can also be used to help make decisions for patients who are dying.

Avivit was a woman with many faces. Avivit consulted patients on Fridays, provided a lot relevant and non-relevant information and kept nothing to herself. She was radiant in all her glory and gave us detailed explanations of my condition, showed us the pictures, and recommended future actions. She explained that there was a possibility of fractures due to bone metastases. Therefore, it was imperative to not exert any effort. She recommended Zomera as a novel treatment for strengthening the bones. She stated that the treatment was effective and that it wasn't subsidized so that we could probably buy it privately.

Avivit let us ask four questions at the end of our meeting. However, she actually had all the information we needed. Avivit recommended that I meditate. Studies have shown that meditation has a longer life expectancy than patients who don't meditate. Meditation releases endorphins in the brain. She understood that I had had enough of my anus being shoved up by my fingers and gave me a non-invasive physical exam. The meeting was pleasant and friendly. During the checkup she asked me about my profession and I shared information about the dairy farm. She was a big fan of Teva Ez cheese and a general lover of goat cheese. Avivit liked my Naot shoes, and said that "He who wears eco-friendly shoes must be a good person." I disagree with that statement.

We were amazed by her depth of knowledge and, even more, her willingness to share her time with us. This was unlike previous experts who charged high consultation fees and kept their knowledge to themselves. We agreed that Avivit would become my chief consultant in all matters relating to cancer. Ruthie was asked to pay Ruthie a consultation fee, or at the very least a donation. Ruthie called me the next day to inform me that she would trade a cheese delivery for the barter. Ruthie welcomed us home and prepared soup and burekas4 from the items she'd purchased on her way. In some ways, I felt fortunate. If I was destined to die, I would have a supportive and empowering environment just like the one that I had. I hummed Chava Alberstein's song "London Doesn't Wait For Me" which was a good fit for my current state of mind.

Two processes can occur in bone that has been damaged by cancerous metastasis. One is osteolytic (bone destroying) and the other is osteoblastic (bone building). Rebuilding the bone that has been damaged does not result in a healthy bone, but it can cause a deformed bone.

The osteoclast is the demolisher cell. It suckers calcium from bones and causes bone disintegration. This process can lead to the collapse of central bones in the skeleton, such as the spine and pelvis, in extreme cases of bone metastases. Zomera stops or significantly reduces osteoclastic activity and restores calcium balance to a normal state. It significantly reduces bone pain and prevents the bone from separating. It is considered a life-saving drug.

Ironically, the drug's name in English is "Zometa". The Israeli branch of the company was concerned that the name might be misinterpreted, particularly among female patients. Zometa, in Hebrew, means "She died", so they changed the name to Zomera.

— ◊ —

While in the hospital I decided that I didn't want to go back to Dr. Solan after he failed me to diagnose and treat my illness. I knew that I needed a new GP. Nabil Hatib, a doctor we met at the hospital, was our new GP.

Ma'alot Health Clinic. We found out that he was very patient-biased. He did many tests and made no mistakes. This approach claims that testing costs are cheaper than treating an illness that is not caught in time. It's a way to cut down on testing. He was a friendly man who tried to make the patient feel comfortable in all medical and bureaucratic procedures. This was often more difficult for the patient than his illness. This was evident in the way Dr. Solan dealt with my request to rush the tests that he wanted me take.

In meeting other doctors, I sometimes felt like they were "establishmentbiased": The establishment is their employer; therefore, they are indebted to it. In an effort to reduce costs, they reduced the number of tests, drugs, and possibly even the information that was vital to the patient. I was impressed by Dr. Nabil Hatib's explanations and decided to make the transfer. Since then, Dr. Hatib never failed me. He is always responsive to my needs and will try to meet my unusual and not-so-odd request time and again. He is a great help in getting approvals for various drugs and treatments.

As part of my hormonal treatments, I was required to have a Zoladex injection once every three months. The prescription had to be placed in advance at the main pharmacy of the clinic. It was sent to Nahariya where it was picked up by me and taken to Dr. Nabil, who then injected it. It took time and effort to get the drugs and have the treatments completed. Special drugs needed to be ordered from the central pharmacy prior to the date of use. Also, someone needed to make sure that all injections and treatments are done on time. It was quite scary to get a Zoladex injection. The hypodermic needle measures approximately 3 millimeters in thickness and contains a hard substance. It is injected under the skin into the abdomen. It melts in three months so it is not necessary to douse as often. Dr. Nabil told me that he didn't have any experience with the injection, but that he would give it a try. The injection went well. It was a short and sharp pain. The substance was right under my skin. I was able to leave the room quickly.

Dr. Nabil also printed me my medical file, because I was contemplating filing a negligence claim against Dr. Solan or the HMO clinic. The medical file was not what I expected. Many of my previous complaints were not documented and some were written in shorthand. For example, the 1995 complaint about frequent urination wasn't recorded. It was not recorded because the doctor verbally referred to me to the nurse for sugar testing. The test came back normal so he sent me on my way. A lawyer who dealt with medical claims advised me that the results must be weighed against what an average doctor would have done in my case. The ministry of health instructed me to check anyone over the age of 50. I was probably a year too young. Because I was too young to have this type of cancer, it seemed that a reasonable doctor would also act as he did. Avivit advised me to not deal with it and to save my energy for fighting the disease. I found this only partially logical. How would managing a medical malpractice affect my ability to fight the illness? It could cause me to forget to take my medication. Would my injection not arrive on time? But I was aware that fighting cancer, even though it is somewhat complicated, requires a lot of emotional strength. I took her advice and let go.

One time, as I was arriving at the HMO clinic Nahariya to undergo lab tests, Dr. Solan approached me. He tried to hug but I shoved him away. I was then welcomed into his office by him. He sat down in the same self-confident position that I remember from my previous visits with him. I was free to unleash all my frustrations on him. I made my argument quietly, yet assertively. I explained to him that he had failed in one of the most important ways a doctor can fail: saving lives. His body language changed dramatically after hearing the words. As I attacked him, he sat down in a chair and seemed very miserable. He claimed that I was too young for suspicion that I had prostate cancer. Also, that screenings are not done until the age of 50, while

I was only 49 years old. He said something along the lines of, "Well, I've said all you wanted to." I felt that I had to express myself clearly and not try to offend him. I was pleased with my presentation, phrasing and performance. I did not feel any relief from anger, elation or the like.

— ◊ —

It was evident that the treatment was working. My physical condition was improving and my limping, which was evident before I was admitted, disappeared completely. It was now much easier to walk. I felt good again. Despite the cloud of sadness that hung over my head, I was content. We took our regular evening stroll through the neighborhood, taking part in an inner road that ran through beautiful forests surrounding our village. When we were together, our main topic of conversation was my cancer issues. I analyzed and discussed the issues, trying to make sense of them. Rivka was not a very active participant, but she did speak a lot. Rivka simply said, "We're going save you" at one point during our walk. It was quite surprising. I was shocked to learn that the grim diagnosis and the dire prognoses were not what I wanted. I believed I was going to die quickly. Rivka's simple statement opened up a new world of possibility. She said it naturally and without any hint of insincerity. These five words were a great encouragement to me. It was as if someone was always there for me, no matter what.

— ◊ —

It had been over a month since my discharge from the hospital. My fiftieth year was fast approaching. This is a major anniversary that only happens once in a life time. Rivka and me talked about our plans for celebrating my birthday before I fell ill. On numerous occasions, I mentioned to Rivka that I would love to travel to India. I was aware of her dislike for dirty places so I assumed she wouldn't agree. It turned out that she didn't want to hear about it. We never decided how to celebrate. Everything was changed by my illness.

Rivka asked me kindly after I had left the hospital how I wanted to celebrate my birthday. "At El Hama6 springs," Rivka asked me. I replied because warm water helped with my pain and general well-being. I didn't have to add anything. The family's well-oiled machine was in motion. Rivka's sister Galit went to the Golan Heights to inspect the guesthouses, near El-Hama. She returned from the Golan Heights with a strong recommendation for Kfar Haruv resort.

We booked Wednesday, November 28th and Thursday, Nov 29th. Because I was due to receive my first Zomera treatment that day, we chose these dates. Arieh and Dina joined us at Kfar Haruv to celebrate my birthday, but this was not my knowledge. Rivka advised me that they would cancel my payment, pay for the guesthouse, and book one night for themselves. It was a great surprise to find out that they would be joining us. They were so much fun to spend time with. They were always so busy. I hoped this would give me the chance to enjoy some time of stress-free leisure with them.

Tuesday was the first day I received Zomera to strengthen my bones. Since the drug was not subsidized, I had to pay for it myself. The prescription I received at the hospital was sufficient to order the Zomera several days in advance. After verifying that the medication had arrived at the main pharmacy I drove to the location, presented my prescription and gave my credit card to the pharmacist. The pharmacist charged me over $500 for the drug and gave me the small package in blue and white. It contained the substance to curb my bone metastases. I quickly fled to the hospital to receive this costly and potentially beneficial drug via IV.

I was about to enter the treatment room of the oncological hospital for the first time as patient. As I entered the room, I felt both uneasy and curious. It was fascinating to see the workings of this horrible business. After I had completed the registration and was admitted, I was allowed to enter the treatment room. There were about ten armchairs, with patients and their families seated on them. It was easy to identify who was the patient and who the family member was by the IV needles that were inserted into the veins. Two more rooms were located at the opposite end of the treatment area. They had hospital beds and were separated by curtains. These were for people with more severe conditions, those who could not stand up and needed to be able to lie down while receiving treatment. Some of the patients looked as though they were dying. I used all my strength to try to get away from them. I didn't take on their suffering. This ability to take myself out of my own misery is what I believed I had. This must be a defense mechanism that I have created to protect my strength in my own fight. Soon, I would have a needle inserted in my vein with chemical substances flowing into my bloodstream. Their lives would be dependent upon them. They would have to do the job, save me or help me fight the scum who has been attacking my body. Nobody knew the answer, or even talked about it. It is so bizarre. It was so strange. Until then, every time I got sick, I knew that certain medications would cure me. Now, however, no one could predict the outcome or guarantee its success.

I was introduced to the nurses on the ward. Ann was the one who took care of me. I gave Ann the Zomera packet and she sat down in one of the armchairs provided by the treatment room. Ann rolled in a treatment cart, filled the bags with various substances and then hung them on an IV stand. Ann was the first to ask Ann for her patient's name in order to avoid mistakes. After verifying it was me, Ann inserted the needle in my vein and connected the first bag. It contained a cleaning product. She switched the bags shortly after and hooked me up with the real thing. The Zomera started to slowly enter my bloodstream for the first time in my entire life. For the full Zomera dose, it is recommended to inject within fifteen minutes. Ann hooked me back up to the cleaning solution once more after the bag was empty. This would allow the Zomera remaining in my bloodstream to be washed out completely. Ann gave me a date for my next treatment within four weeks. I thanked her and I left.

I felt bad towards the end of the evening and realized it was likely side effects of the drug. Although the nurse and doctor mentioned side effects that could occur from the drug, I didn't think too much about it. By the evening, I felt worse. I crawled into my bed. My entire body was aching the next morning and I felt like I was about to die. We drove to Kfar Haruv to celebrate my 50th birthday. Rivka drove, and I was completely exhausted in the passenger seat. We reached Kfar Haruv and I ran to my bed. I couldn't leave it. Rivka, Arieh and Dina were concerned and would do anything to make my life better. They thought I was going to die. They took me to El-Hama springs which helped a bit. Dina and Arieh went home. Soon after they left, my feelings started to improve. It was like I had regained my life. Retrospectively, I realize that Zomera can cause flu-like symptoms in patients who take it for the first time. You can reduce these symptoms by simply taking Tylenol or another pain reliever. Despite being warned at the hospital about it, I didn't feel it and it caused me great suffering.

I requested that the Zomera medication be covered by the health services. Their pharmaceutical committee received the form. The request was denied. I attached the recommendations of the relevant doctors to the form. This meant that we would have to pay an extra $500 per month. Ruthie advised us to not give up. Next, I approached the regional health care provider.

Every month, my blood tests showed an improvement. The treatments worked. This was encouraging. However, the thought that the hormonal treatments would cease to be effective at some point was a heavy burden on my shoulders. It brought me unease in my daily life.

Another refusal by the health service to fund Zomera was made by the regional doctor. His explanation was that the drug was still experimental for patients like me. Zomera was not approved for bone metastases caused by prostate cancer. This was in addition to the refusal from another health care entity that I had previously received, which stated that there was no evidence of clinical research that would support the use of the drug in my particular case. These excuses seemed like they were being used to save money by the health service, especially as I had attached a 13-page checklist supporting the use of the drug with patients in my situation. The health clinic doctor claimed that he wasn't authorized to approve certain medications.

Frustrating. They didn't have a clinical basis for the drug, and then the doctor wasn't authorized to make a decision. Now they are telling me that the drug was experimental. I was not ready to give up. After years of having additional coverage, I realized that it was not logical for me to pay for the drug that I needed for my own health. Next, I approached the director of the clinic with Avivit and a letter.

---

4 Filo dough is a savory pastry made from filo dough.

5 A famous Israeli singer-songwriter.

6 Israel's most famous hot springs attraction.CHAPTER FIVE

A SICK ROUTINE:
LEARNING TO GET BETTER WITH DAILY LIFE

Mid-February 2002

Mitzpe Hila was visited by a new couple. The couple rented the house of our neighbors who had moved to the United States. The alternative medicine clinic was run by Dr. Herr and located in Haifa. Rivka tried to help me by consulting Dr. Herr. He offered three options for alternative medicine to me: Chinese acupuncture and naturopathy. He even offered to do the Chinese acupuncture. Dr. Herr suggested that I see one of the two doctors he knew to help me find a naturopath. He also provided details about experts in supplements.

Most of his suggestions were accepted by me. Although my first Chinese acupuncture treatment was unpleasant, it is possible to stay healthy. Dr. Herr promised me a second treatment in three to one month.

I made an appointment to see Dr. Dan Keret in a village near the middle of Israel. Rivka joined me. I was able to discuss the best nutrition for men in my situation. Dr. Keret explained that both prostate cancer and other forms of cancer can be caused by fat, especially animal fat. He gave the example of the people in Southeast Asia who consume very little animal products and have rare cases of prostate cancer. He suggested a strict vegan diet that is low in fat, with the exception of fish. Avocado was exempted due to its high amount of vegetable fat. He also suggested North Sea fish such as tuna and salmon. Because they are rich in Omega-3 fatty acid that can improve bodily function, as well as cruciferous vegetables like cauliflower, broccoli, and other beans such white beans, garbanzo bean, soy beans and white beans. He advised me to avoid processed foods like cereal and the similar.

I thought, "Wow, here comes another blow." In addition to what I have already dealt with, I must now avoid my favorite foods, such as shawarma, 7-steak, pork, dairy products, cakes, and chocolate. How can I sustain this?

Dr. Keret suggested that my next sessions be dedicated to emotional support and fortification. I agreed. I agreed to it, even though my emotions were shaky. It was an interesting encounter and I felt like we had a lot in common.

Rivka assumed her new role with great dedication. We had to do everything possible to save me, so Rivka went full force. She quickly became a specialist in vegan cuisine, and adhered to my strict dietary requirements. I moved to a new phase of my life, going vegan almost completely. It was not what my body and soul wanted, but I gave up all meat and dairy.

There are many books that discuss the importance of eating a healthy, lean diet, low in animal fats and high in vegetables, fruits, and beans. These are my two favorite books:

1 *Natural Medicine: How to Prevent and Treat Cancer* by Dr. Michael Murray, Dr. Tim Birdsall and Dr. Joseph E. Pizzorno are Dr. Paul Reilly.

2 *Dr. Fuhrman, Eat to Live.*— ◊ —

Two months after the initial treatment, the hormonal treatment took effect. I experienced new pains almost every day during that time. Each new pain caused panic in us and we ran to the doctor. It was once swollen glands that I thought were metastases. It was another time intense stomach pain, and other serious straits. They were probably the result of hormonal and nutritional changes that my body was going through.

My right leg was hurting for a few nights. My pelvis was on the right side, and I felt the pain. This was the location of the largest metastasis, according to the bone scan. This was the main source of my problems. I followed Dr. Ruthie's advice and took a 10-milligram OxyContin, which is a painkiller. Rivka and Ruthie believed that one should not suffer if one can take a painkiller. They thought I was dying soon, and I suspected that they believed I would die quickly. I decided to let them know that I could live comfortably and painlessly my final days.

Truth be told, I felt like I was taking a drug for the first time. I was anxious to fly high after I swallowed that pills. Although nothing like that happened, I did sleep well that night. But, I woke up dizzy and drowsy the next morning. My conscience started to nag at me. Maybe I had taken the pill too late or not enough water. I wasn't sure if I should drive or not. I eventually left for the dairy late, but I was still inactive the majority of the day. I continued to feel dizzy and drowsy. It also started to hurt my upper abdomen, which I assumed was an side effect of the drug.

I decided to finish my day early and took the Haj sisters, who were working in the dairy, with me back to their village at around one o'clock. They wanted me to be there early for a memorial at their mosque for their grandfather who had died forty-days earlier.

It was difficult to drive home. I was still feeling drowsy at the time I arrived, and I couldn't understand why. I fell asleep for two hours before going to bed. I awoke in the evening with upper abdominal pain. I promised myself that I would not take the cheeky pill again unless I was absolutely desperate.

— ◊ —

Rivka and me met Dr. Keret again. As usual, I used the opportunity to make deliveries for the dairy. I delivered one batch of cheese to a customer and received packing materials from the factory that makes them.

Dr. Keret said that the role of a naturopath was to improve my emotional strength to fight the disease effectively. He agreed that drugs and emotional support were important components of the healing process. It was obvious that it is more difficult for someone to deal with a crisis when their spirits are low. I was also privileged to have him dedicate an hour and a quarter to me.

You won't find such dedicated attention anywhere else. Rivka sat in the room and listened passively to our conversations. It was a great experience to have her there. It allowed her to see my hardships and the strength I displayed despite them.

I shared with him my journal and my difficulties in expressing my emotions. I was actually writing this for my computer. He asked me how vulnerable I allowed myself to be in my writing and I replied that I was about 98 percent. He explained that the more exposure I had, the more my writing would move me and how it would appeal to others. I decided to follow his advice and try to be more transparent in my writing.

We won on Tuesday, March 26, 2002, three months after I began my fight to have my Zomera funded by the health services. The health services called me to inform me that funding was available for the drug. Although the funding was only for three months, and with 15% of the cost still covered by me, there was no doubt that we had established a precedent and I would be able in the future to have the drug funded again by them. It was not only financial relief but also a victory against the establishment. I was the first person with prostate cancer to receive treatment at the expense of the health system. I wasn't the only one fighting this battle. Good friend Dr. Ruthie was there to help me fight the battle as well as organize the professional materials. Dr. Avivit was also a tremendous help, giving me articles supporting the use of the drug for patients with my condition and writing a support letter to the CEO. This complicated campaign was also supported by good friends. It was sweet to taste victory, especially when it was a just victory for the small citizen over this system.

Ruthie called me to inform her of the news. I also said that I was grateful for the financial assistance and that they had accepted my justified argument. As the holiday was approaching, we wished each other a Happy Passover. Rivka was then reached and I told her. I was delighted for her. I called Avivit later and the rest of them.

$$- \Diamond -$$

My time was spent mainly in the dairy. I felt that my emotional burden was reduced by being busy with other things. A computer can mimic the way that a person's mind and heart works. Both seem to be occupied with one task at the time and are unable to handle multiple tasks simultaneously. However, both the human mind as well as a computer can swiftly switch between one task and another. Despite my job at the dairy, I couldn't fully disconnect from my troubling thoughts about my illness. However, handling the dairy affairs helped to ease the burden.

Dror and me outlined some tasks to improve the dairy products and made them our top priority. We were both curious about how we could make this happen. This was something I knew had to be done, despite the financial strain. A factory that doesn't invest in its own technological advancement will not progress, which means it will fall behind as competitors move ahead. So we had no choice but to invest and move on.

Zvi, a neighbor and friend, was there to greet me when I returned home. He invited me and my family to dinner. Many people have taken an interest in my condition and have offered their assistance or given me more attention. It was almost as if I were a celebrity. Some people stayed away from me because they were unsure of what to do or how to respond to someone "sentenced to die." They may have been afraid that the cancer would stick to them. I did not know I wanted to live with them for many more years.

Was determination enough? Yes, I had the most amazing team, the latest drugs, the best treatments and God to help me. All of this was enough. Who knew?

We left the dinner feeling like something was missing. It didn't work out and it was difficult to establish intimacy with him. This intimacy is only possible through deep friendship. Rivka also became mad at me towards the end of the evening, as I had mentioned that some of our neighbors were about to divorce. It had been a few days since she had spoken to me about it, so it wasn't inappropriate for her to tell me. I was annoyed by her anger and there was a silence between us. The restrained anger continued throughout the day. This illness and my obsession with it often raised tensions between us to a level we didn't know before. It's no surprise that many marriages end when one partner becomes ill. Rivka's needs were my responsibility and I should have taken more care of her. All the hype was about me and not her.

My energy levels began to drop dramatically. I was unable to work as hard and resisted the urge to waste energy.

Hormonal treatment can cause fatigue and exhaustion. It reduces hemoglobin levels in the blood, among other things. The hemoglobin transports oxygen from the blood to various cells. The feeling is not affected by sleep or rest.

— ◊ —

Since my diagnosis with prostate cancer, it had been more than three months. To keep my momentum, I wrote almost every day. Writing hours were often after ten at night. These were hours when each member of the family was doing his own thing. It was very convenient for me. It had two drawbacks. First, Rivka was already asleep and I was quite tired. She was already asleep by the time I got into bed.

We decided to invite Dr. Avivit, and Dr. Ruthie to lunch as a gesture of gratitude and appreciation for their incredible help. Avivit brought her eight-year-old daughter, while Avivit came with her husbands. She was smart, active, and vibrant, just like her mother. My father, two of my brothers and their partners were also invited. Rivka loved preparing this event.

There wasn't a dull moment, the conversation just flowed. Everyone enjoyed talking.

Avivit noticed that I only ate vegan food and no dairy products. When Avivit asked me about it, I replied that I was following the advice of the naturopath and that he believed it could help me fight cancer. This theory was completely discredited by her. She claimed that if I had started to eat this diet twenty- or thirty years ago, it might have prevented the development of cancer. It didn't work because I was already sick. She argued the opposite. My emotional strain was already very high from trying to follow this diet. You are a brilliant and practical woman! This simple argument convinced me and clarified for me the importance of reducing my emotional stress. She suggested that I eat a healthy diet for a man my age. This included eating lots of fruits and vegetables, avoiding fried foods and food with hydrogenated oils, choosing whole wheat and brown rice, avoiding sugar, and not avoiding dairy and meat products.

I accepted her suggestions and was able to get rid of the restrictive diet that was so difficult for me.

— ◊ —

After returning from work at three, I decided to change the oil in my car. I was careful to leave a gap in the garage floor when we built our house in Mitzpe Hila. This allowed me to reach underneath the car. Then, something happened. It took me a while to find a replacement key for the special key that opens the oil screw. To open the oil lid, I had to exert a lot of physical effort. This was something I didn't want to do. Even moderate effort caused me pain in my bones. Because I enjoy doing technical jobs, and because I'm stubborn, I kept working despite being frustrated. While one part of me thought I was reckless and took a huge risk, another part of me reminded me how much these jobs were a joy and how much I love them. I was able to enjoy the joy of creativity through this task. It is not worth living if all things are forbidden. Everything would be fine if I was careful, did things slowly and consciously, and that was all. It would be a proof to myself that I was still alive and active. Being active also made me more emotionally strong and gave me a lot satisfaction.

One of my neighbors passed me as I was finishing the job. As if to say, "Look at me!" I stood tall and walked toward him with a healthy air. I felt a sudden surge of happiness.

— ◊ —

My youngest son Guri was with me to the Haifa youth soccer team practice. His team plays against other youth teams every weekend. He practices three days a week. He asked me today to accompany him to the game. I gladly agreed. Because of my condition, I hadn't seen him play for a while. I felt that we both needed it. We became closer because of those trips and my interest in him. That was worth all the effort. He was a good player and scored a goal. It was so exciting! I was so proud! He told me on the way back that he couldn't see me among the crowd but that he heard the whistles, and knew it was I.

Rivka and other children went out to eat in a nearby Arab village after the game. I enjoyed barbecued meat despite my strict diet. The flavor of the meat was strange to me and I didn't enjoy it as much. Was it guilt?

— ◊ —

It was a difficult day. My stomach hurt again. Ruthie thought I should call Avivit to see what she would do. It was probably because of the meal I had at the restaurant the day before. I decided to wait. Since my PSA level was 1.3, everything should have been okay. This indicated that my hormonal treatment was working well and that the illness was slowly receding.

Rivka was informed by me that I wasn't feeling well after I had returned from the dairy in the afternoon. It was likely her fault. Tsemer, which means "wool in Hebrew), was our dog who attacked our neighbor two days ago. That neighbor happens to be my Chinese acupuncturist. The dog was taken to a shelter by the owner, who left it there. She did not tell me and told the children to keep it secret. The dog was a gift for Bat-El's eleventh Birthday. She loved it very much. Tsemer became a lunatic recently and started to bark at passersby, and even bit some of them. We had to tie her up.

We would let her go from midnight to the early hours of the morning when traffic was light in the area. I asked my family to refrain from releasing her during the day. My instructions were not fully followed. Rivka let loose that morning. The neighbor attacked the dog and went into Rivka's backyard. The man demanded a large monetary settlement. I only learned of the situation after the dog went missing. I was shocked. I felt great anger at having these events kept from me. Rivka seemed to be growing apart from me and isolating myself from my home life, right when I needed her support. It felt like I was losing my voice in my home and being powerless in even the simplest of things. There were other grudges that surfaced in these situations. I was able to let loose of some steam through a conversation we had.

A few days back, I began reading Cancer as a turning point, which my naturopath recommended. I was lifted by the first few chapters and filled with hope. It featured stories of people who had overcome cancer well and were able to recover. There was also information about emotional support to heal the body. The last chapters dealt with the possibility of death and how to prepare for it. I was fascinated by the section on death preparation, but it was too much for me. Did I make it all the way? I did not let myself feel that I was going to death. Yes, I am sick but I feel quite good so far. I am employed and have many goals for the future. That dark cloud that hangs over me is always there and can blow right in my face at any moment.

Today, we moved the dairy offices out of Dror's home to the new dairy building. The new office was situated in the gallery above the production area. This gave me immense satisfaction. This also allowed us to control production more effectively. Although there were some missing items, like a desk and a cabinet, it was still very spacious. It was made from insulated panels so it was comfortable to work in. My only problem was the fact that I had to climb 17 stairs, which was quite difficult for me. I was able to climb the stairs by using the railing. It was okay, I would take it.

— ◊ —

My right leg was very painful last night. This is probably because of the metastasis to my right pelvis. The pain started suddenly, most often at night, but it was gone by the end of the day. Due to the pain, I was up since 3 AM. The following words echoed through my mind as I lay awake, unable to sleep:

It's almost all I need

A good wife
Great kids
Beautiful house with a private backyard

Interesting things to do
Enough money
Enough assets
But
I have osteoblastic activity within my bones

Also osteoclastic activity

I have prostate carcinoma
In short, I have cancer.

I don't have a lover

Syphilis is not something I have.

I don't have the flu

And I don't have a cold

Eczema is not a problem for me

*But I don't have an orgasm. I
don't have a life?*

The new dairy office was completed. Dror built a bathroom on the second floor because I am not able to climb stairs. It was a wonderful experience that made me feel warm and comforted. Dror is a wonderful person who can offer assistance when needed. We prepared a suitable sewer line during construction. Now all that was left to do was install a door, close the walls and place a toilet bowl. To put in the walls we used the leftover construction material. This was very simple and left us with only the sanitary dishes to install.

I was able to hear what was happening on the production floor from the new office in the gallery above the dairy. This allowed me to better understand the workings of the dairy. Arab workers shouted at the radio in Arabic. Fairuz, a Lebanese singer, was often heard. Her most loved job was at the dairy. Even though I didn't understand Arabic, I knew what she was talking about. Most of her songs were broken heart love songs and longing for someone. I fell in love with her songs over time and loved listening to them again and again. I was also able to memorize all local commercials and promotions.

Later, I had to purchase envelops and salmon for Guri's Bar Mitzvah invites. I also had to buy a few items for the dairy. I felt overwhelmed by the fatigue and depression that had characterized my current state, and needed to take a break. I ordered a cappuccino from a nearby coffee shop and a croissant. I was satiated with the fatty croissant, but it made me feel guilty. After a few minutes, I felt better.

— ◊ —

My brother Arieh and Dina, his wife, came to dinner last night. They also brought my father. It was delicious. My father doesn't interfere in my cancer concerns, so he was comfortable helping Rivka fix the family tree he had prepared for his genealogy project. Yes, Rivka is patient and has great skills in dealing with older people. Everyone got bored at some point. The dialogue quickly grew when I started to tell them about my illness, and the journal that I kept. I shared with them the book Cancer as a Turning Point that I was currently reading. One chapter dealt with the difficulty of parting ways from loved ones who are about to die. The author suggested that family members have open conversations about their loved ones' feelings and conditions. People avoided speaking to people dying about their feelings or their imminent death. Instead, they focused on the technical details of things like "Would it be nice to have some tea?" Are you cold? Do you need a blanket? Since then, I feel guilty for not being there for her as much as I should. Now that I think about it, I remember giving her a back rub once to ease her pain. So that she wouldn't be alone, I also slept next to her one night. It's not like I did everything I was supposed.

It was mid-February outside. Rain always makes me joyful. It is my agricultural gene. I hoped that lightening wouldn't strike and destroy the computer like it did in the past.

Yoav, my nephew informed me today that he had completed the second stainless-steel desk for the dairy. He would deliver it tomorrow. Because I was expecting a child at the same time as him, I feel special feelings for him. When I think about it, sometimes I can see Yoav's child. We share a special bond and I love him deeply. Yoav suffered severe injuries while serving in the military on his way to a Lebanon ambush. Hezbollah8 had already known about the planned ambush location and prepared a counter-ambush. A powerful explosive exploded upon their arrival and heavy fire was unleashed on them.

Yoav was killed by his commander and other fighters. He suffered severe wounds that he has never fully recovered from. He was now a skilled artisan and craftsman, working with wood and metals. I was able to use his talents and goodwill to furnish the dairy.

Yoav arrived with the desk he had built in steel. His work was meticulous and precise down to the last detail. He helped me get my Zoladex injection at the health clinic after we had put it together. We were both young, but I enjoyed spending time together.

Three months ago, Dr. Nabil in Ma'alot administered the injection. I drove to Nahariya's health clinic so Nurse Hagar, who I know for years, could give the injection. Last time I was there, I explained to her that the company selling the drug had an instructional video about how to inject it. She dismissed me, "It's okay." "I am very skilled in administering the injection."

Nurse Hagar instructed me to lie down on my stomach and expose my stomach. I received injections by looking away at the needle as it pricked. It made things a lot easier. However, the prick continued for far too long. It was very painful and felt like she was digging into my stomach. I was unable to control my emotions and grabbed her hand, begging her to stop. She could not insert the needle into my skin. The drug was almost out of the needle. However, she claimed that she was able to draw the needle back into the syringe. She was very sorry and apologized, telling me that I had elephant skin. Her second attempt did not go as well. She said it was fine and then told me to take a break for a while before she left.

Yoav and I went to Nahariya's hummus restaurant. We had been there before, and he wanted to go back. We enjoyed the winter sun as we sat outside. It was a joy to see my nephew, who is twenty-five years older than me, spending an hour with us over a plate full of hummus.

I took a photocopy of the bone scan results after we parted ways. I wanted to attach them to the forms I had to file with the disability committee. Patients with cancer who have had chemotherapy or radiation are entitled to 100 percent disability. I would be exempt from income tax if they gave me a

90-100-percent disability. This would cover the large expenses that this illness had cost me. All of this running caused me pain in my right side groin. I was both afraid and angry by this metastasis. I tried to find ways to get rid of it. Perhaps I could freeze, burn or seal it with some material that would stop it getting oxygen and thus destroy it. This illness would end me in one way or another. Either the metastasis would kill me and cause havoc in my body or I would succumb to exhaustion from time to time.

I went back to the office, removed the gauze pads that the nurse had placed on the area and then returned to work. To my horror, the drug meant to be injected under the skin was not on the pad. Nurse Hagar boasted of her expertise in injecting the drug. I was furious. It was an issue of life or death in my case. I was able to find the stick in the pad. I immediately called her and explained what had happened. I was told to apologize and ask for a second prescription by her doctor. I phoned Dr. Nabil to tell him about the incident. He immediately faxed me a prescription. The cost of the injection was approximately $2,600. I had planned to visit Dr. Nabil the next day to have it administered by him.

— ◊ —

The children were watching the soccer match between Germany and Israel on the TV. The kids were happy, laughing and having fun. Reminiscing on the endless joy I had as a child, and how I played and hailed around like them, I began to think back. As we age, our ability to live life fully and enjoy it as fully as we did in childhood diminishes.

Tonight, I'd take a painkiller for the pain in my groin to help me sleep better.

7 Middle Eastern dish mainly made from lamb.

8 A terrorist Islamist group in Lebanon fighting for Israel's existence.
CHAPTER SIX

MEETING NADIR:
PSA: THE END OF THE SLOPE & THE RISE

Late February to Mid-May 2002

Today, I received my last test results from my health clinic.

Good News—Excellent Results.

The PSA reading fell to 0.5. The alkalinephosphatase also dropped to the normal range. My hemoglobin and blood count were both low. However, this was probably a side effect from the hormonal treatment. This type of treatment can have many annoying side effects. This is why I hoped to be able to stop hormonal treatment. If the disease is currently in remission, and the PSA has been low for a prolonged period of time, it is possible.

— ◊ —

Before every Zomera treatment, I met with Dr. Rassan. Dr. Rassan would review my latest test results and ask me questions about how I was feeling. Then he would give instructions for the next treatment. After reviewing my test results, Dr. Rassan decided to do a rectal exam. He wanted to, in other words, push his fingers up my anus yet again. This was an invasive exam, often accompanied by a strong odor. The upside was that I felt the prostate tumor had decreased in size compared to previous examinations. It was felt during the exam and confirmed by the doctor. Based on the most recent positive results, I asked the doctor if I would be able to take a break. It was standard practice to stop the treatment at times. There were two main reasons I wanted to stop it. The first was to prevent the tumor from escaping the hormonal treatment and bursting out again. I wanted to eliminate the terrible side effects, such as impotency, hot flashes and fatigue. It would have been great to get sex again. My enthusiasm was tempered by the doctor who told me that I still had a ways to go and that it was important that we make sure that my results last.

He asked me to not be concerned, as the treatment would have an ongoing effect. He also told me that I had no reason for anxiety. These messages were repeated in every meeting. However, it was completely contrary to all published articles. Because the doctors' predictions were correct, I felt comfortable holding on to his words. I felt pretty good when I got back. My situation had stabilized. I was able to continue living. Although the metastasis to my right pelvis was a bother, especially at night, I could live with it.

I went to the treatment room to receive the monthly Zomera injection into my vein. The room was crowded with advanced cancer patients. One young Arab woman was deaf and mute. Two women accompanied her. She began to cry when one of the women left. The other caressed her and soothed her like a baby. A bald man was also present in the bathroom. He grunted and gurgled dreadfully and also made a lot of noises. To be able to focus on my own needs, I decided to separate myself from the suffering of others patients. It was impossible to choose another option. The entire process took approximately two hours. My treatment lasted for about twenty minutes.

— ◇ —

My veins were beginning to collapse and it was becoming more difficult to insert the needle. They poked my vein twice per month to do blood tests, and once to inject Zomera. It became difficult and uncomfortable to insert the needle into my vein over time. This was another side effect of hormonal treatment. It was hoped that it would not get worse.

After treatment, I went to Haifa to meet with the lawyer who was handling the claim against us made by our neighbor for being bitten by our dog. We had insurance that covered that as well. He planned to sue us for damages.

Next, I attended a meeting with the prostate cancer support group. These meetings were very important to me. I was able to gather and cross-reference information that was crucial to my understanding. I wanted as much detail as possible. Because I was fighting for my own life, it made me feel more likely to defeat this scum.

Dr. Gal, a friendly doctor and expert on prostate issues, was present to discuss the topic and answer questions. I asked him about overseas treatment and he confirmed my previous knowledge. In cases similar to mine, the Israeli treatments were superior. Some centers in the world are able to offer innovative treatments, so it is worth looking into them. One Boston medical facility specialized in treating a particular type of brain cancer. The high cost of such treatment could run into the hundreds of thousands of dollars, he said. He said that even in the most dire cases, there are times when it is worth considering a trial. This information was consistent with what Shmulik (Rabbi Fuhrer's equal) had said to me. He suggested that I participate in atrial after the hormonal treatment stopped working. Avivit's view was almost identical. I realized that there was no need to seek salvation abroad and that I was receiving the best treatment in Israel. It was crucial to understand the difference between "the best possible" and "the very best". It was possible for better treatments to exist elsewhere in the world. However, I accepted the advice of the experts to continue treatment in Israel.

A blood sample was taken by the doctor from us as part of an international study to determine common genetics among prostate cancer patients. They wanted to find a genetic pattern in healthy people that could lead to future illness. They would be able to monitor and detect these individuals early, so that genetic methods could possibly reverse this trend in the future.

He said that my fatigue was due to hormonal treatment.

After I returned to my home, I began to investigate the cause of my fatigue. It was the mornings when I took my Casodex daily hormone pill. By noon, I felt fatigued. Is the pill responsible for my fatigue? I took it at night and let my fatigue build up over the next few days. The fatigue disappeared within a few days. It was working. It was amazing! It was amazing.

Dr. Gal also recommended physical exercise. I asked Dr. Gal if there were any concerns that the increased blood flow could cause cancerous cells spread to other parts of the body. Although he was aware of this argument, he said that there wasn't a similar theory. He suggested that I walk, after I explained my physical limitations. He suggested that I take my wife for an evening walk. We took his advice and went for a long walk the next evening. Although I was happy with myself, I felt the pain from my metastasis returned.

— ◊ —

That night, I couldn't fall asleep. I woke up at 2 AM and thought about taking a painkiller. I looked at the directions and realized that it must be taken with food. I decided to give up on the idea and instead drank hot water. Then, I went back to sleep. My cousin Zivit taught me relaxation techniques and I fell asleep until the next morning. These relaxation exercises allowed me to bring my awareness to one part of my body at a given time. It sent a pleasant, sleepy sensation to the area. The pain was less when I concentrated on the notorious metastasis. These exercises were something I tried every night before falling asleep. It didn't always work. Sometimes, I fell asleep halfway through. Zivit advised me that it was better to not do it lying down as it can cause you to fall asleep. This was a great way to fall asleep, and it felt good.

— ◊ —

Rivka and I spoke briefly last night about our situation. Rivka heard about my pain from my metastases, and I said that I was worried they would attack my body. After Amir's bar mitzvah, Avivit or Dr. Rassan, we agreed to retake our tests. Rivka was always there for me when I wasn't feeling well. Rivka held me close to her at night, just as she did when we first met. She treated me as she always did, even when I was feeling good. Love wasn't an obvious component.

— ◊ —

Our son Amir celebrated his bar mitzvah last Saturday at Mitzpe Hila. To prepare for the party, I made a menorah with thirteen candles. This was to correspond to the number of Amir's closest friends. Each person could light a candle. The menorah was made from an olive branch that I had cut off a tree in our yard. I cleaned it, and made holes for the candles. To ensure stability, I attached two legs from thin branches to the structure.

Over 100 guests attended the event. I did my best to look my best. It was more important than ever for me to look my best, to show everyone that I didn't intend to go anywhere. I dyed my graying hair, and was praised for my appearance. Izhar, my brother, asked me why I looked so great. It was the drug that I was taking, I said. He asked me to spare some.

Amir was determined to lead the event. Amir invited all of his family members, including two grandfathers, one grandmother and his brother and sister, as well as aunts and uncles, close friends and us parents, to light a candle. Orr, our oldest son, made a joke of it and congratulated Amir as if he were Amir calling to the Torah. Baruch, my brother in law, showed a slideshow that he had prepared for this event. It featured Amir and was followed by a Capoeira demonstration by the children of the family at the club's entrance. Our village friends folded the tables and chairs for us at the end of the event. The house was filled with my family after the party. Daniel and Dr. Ruthie were also present.

A fundamental question about my PSA bothered me. Could a drop in PSA signify that the disease is in remission? Or could it be that the PSA was dropping as the disease spreads inside my body, allowing the metastases and to grow and develop? Ruthie was kind enough to confirm the matter with Avivit.

Many people were killed in the terrorist attacks that occurred during this time. As we watched the massacres by the Palestinians, we felt helpless. I kept asking myself, "What can we do to stop the madness taking over this region right now?" Our cheese demand was directly affected by the fragile security situation. Goat cheese is naturally very expensive. Our products are also consumed by restaurants and hotels. When their occupancy falls, so does our demand. A second reason is the fact that people tend to be less indulgent during terrorist attacks. February is a particularly poor month for sales. This should change, I believe.

— ◊ —

Technology is taking control of our lives. Since a few days, I've been experiencing computer problems which have forced me to stop writing. Yoel, my best friend, assists me in this matter as well as other matters. When the dairy isn't busy, I use the time to write in my journal. It is amazing to me how strong my desire to write. It is a way to relieve stress and lure me. This is how I imagine an author feeling when writing a new book.

— ◊ —

Ruthie called. Avivit was contacted by Ruthie. My question about the PSA was answered loudly by her. A decreasing PSA means that the disease is in remission. This message was a wonderful surprise to me. It was a sign that my disease was receding. Although I felt a bit relieved, I knew it was temporary. The scum was just around the corner.

— ◊ —

On Sunday, Dr. Dan Keret, a naturopath, was my visit. Rivka couldn't help but to resist me leaving. I decided to go alone this time. Maybe she was tired of me and my cancer. We agreed that I would be better off going it alone. It allowed me to express myself without her interference, even though driving was intimate for us. We would usually go out to eat or go out after the meeting. This allowed us to discuss the events and had quality time together.

It was interesting and perhaps more than any of the previous meetings. Dr. Keret, as usual, asked me about what was new. I shared with him the positive results of my medical examinations and Amir's bar mitzvah. This gave me many happy moments. He was thrilled by my report and the overall improvement. I explained to him that I was still in a bad place and that I felt a cloud of doubt over me because I knew the improvement would be temporary.

Dr. Keret explained to me that he wants to build my immunity so that I can fight cancer with maximum effectiveness. To do that, I need to live my life "eagerly" so that my "soul does not wilt." It is important to only do what I love and to get up each morning ready to complete the task at hand. He believes that this lifestyle increases the life expectancy of patients with severe illnesses and allows them to live more full lives.

This method is illustrated in the book Cancer as a Turning point, which I mentioned earlier. Many examples are provided in the first section of the book of patients with cancer who have successfully used these methods and experienced a significant increase in their life expectancy. Following Dr. Keret's advice, I decided to define for myself what activities I was "eager" and follow the instructions in the book. I chose to devote my time to improving the Teva Ez products and writing my journal. One day a week I would volunteer in a factory for disabled people. Rivka was very supportive of my idea. I was able to rely on her unwavering support in these areas.

Dr. Keret asked me about the activities that I had chosen. I was too enthusiastic to believe he had. I said so. He said that I had earned his compliments and was showing the characteristics of a true survivor. He pulled out a guidebook from his library that listed seven qualities that make someone a survivor. They were listed one by one and I realized that all seven of them were true. Wow! I think I'm going to live a lot longer. Rivka was interested in the story. I was surprised to learn that I couldn't remember any of the seven qualifications. I had to ask Dr. Keret for them.

He said that he had enjoyed the session and parted ways with me at the end. This feedback was rare. I enjoyed the experience. Although I wasn't sure if his help would prolong my life or not, I know it has. I took with me a book about communication between parents, children. His wife treated parents and children, and sold the book. Orr, our son, was the first to read it. He said he was reading it to "know the enemy." His expressions combine sharp observation and humor with a touch of cynicism. This is something I love.

— ◊ —

Yesterday I got the results of my last test. My PSA was now 0.4. This was a good result, but the PSA was slowly declining. The hormonal treatment was nearing its end and it would soon cease affecting me. This would allow the disease to recur. This realization was alarming and disturbed my serenity. My cholesterol was also something I had to be aware of.

Dr. Nabil stated that we could ignore it since I had abstained from animal fat. (Animal fat can cause high cholesterol. He is quite heavy and doesn't exercise as much (as you can see), but he suggested that I walk as much as possible.

The hormonal treatment can also cause an increase in cholesterol or lipids.

— ◊ —

Yesterday we hosted Lenny Hirsch (a fellow patient with prostate cancer) for dinner. He was a friend of the Israel Cancer Association. He was the organizer and founder of the support group for prostate cancer patients, which I had the unfortunate pleasure of being a part. He was a South African man of sixty, intelligent and a walking encyclopedia on prostate cancer issues. He was able to identify patients and doctors from around the globe and knew all of the available treatments and methods by heart. His knowledge was invaluable in helping me gather information. He was the one to tell me about the online forum for patients with prostate cancer. I expressed my desire for membership. I was able to sign up and became a regular member that night. Don Cooley, a fellow American with prostate cancer, founded the forum. There were many sections on the forum, including one for advanced cancer stages like mine. My forum membership was going to allow me to delve deeper into the information that is so important for my success fighting the scum. Lenny was kind enough to thank me for his assistance. We also thanked him for being so accommodating.

Lenny ran a small catering business. He told me before we parted that he was no longer working. I had an idea. Perhaps we could hire him to run our cheese shop.

— ◊ —

Life is complex. Everything would be perfect if...

Yesterday I was able to attend the support group meeting. The guest speaker was Dr. Ed, a specialist in prostate cancer. I asked him the same question as the previous speaker: Did the low PSA mean that the cancer was dormant or not? It meant that the cancer was currently in remission. Actually, I knew my current condition was temporary and it was only a matter time before it changed.

I wish I could find a way to preserve the current state. This "if only" keeps us from reaching "wellness".

Another terror attack occurred this morning in an area inhabited by Israel Arabs. Seven people were killed, and many more were injured. It would be great if there had been no terrorist attacks, peace and even the possibility of finding a solution.

Everything would be so much better if we could increase our sales by 30%. We were developing new products. We would be more successful if they succeeded.

— ◊ —

Another book about cancer was finished by me. It spoke volumes to me. The Transformed Cell is the book by a Jewish-American physician who dedicated his career to finding a cure. His method involves modifying a genetic aspect of the immune system to recruit the body's natural immunity mechanisms, and then destroying tumors. He was able to cure a large number of patients suffering from metastases throughout their bodies. This is something that conventional medicine could not offer. Leah, our American friend, was able to help me locate the doctor. Leah searched online for his information within minutes. He was still working at the American Institute for Cancer Research, even though the book was published 10 years ago. She promised to call him and bring his information with her to Israel when she arrived on Saturday.

It would be so great if I could eliminate this scum!

What did I really ask?

To live, as everyone else.

Everything was obvious up until now.

Everything was suddenly impossible overnight.

— ◊ —

We bought two machines to make new products for the dairy after much discussion. Before making a major investment, there was always some stage of contemplation. I made that decision with all my strength, knowing full well that one cannot move forward without taking risks. I believed we had the financial strength to withstand such risks. That decision was a good one.

The machine was used to make cheese tubes. They were then packed in new packaging with DCA (dynamic controlled environment), which extends their shelf life.

It is likely that the consumer doesn't realize how much work goes into developing and manufacturing each product. He may not be aware of the many people behind each product he purchases. He doesn't care about the price or the flavor of the product.

I was happy to see the efforts we made to promote dairy and bring a modern touch to it, just like a child who receives a new toy. I also set myself high-quality manufacturing goals to take pride in our products and achieve profitability and cushioning. It was a positive feeling that we were moving in the right direction. This gave me great satisfaction.

I remember that my holy goals were to find happiness and satisfaction. I agreed with Dr. Keret about the healing power that they had.

Lenny and I struck up a mutual understanding. He gave me some articles about prostate cancer. Some of these I have read. These articles were written in medical English and required a lot of effort to understand. It was difficult to understand the unfamiliar terms. The business partnership also took a practical turn. Lenny would operate the cheese shop and restaurant next to the dairy on Saturdays. We visited a cheese shop and restaurant in the same style as we were looking to create to get some insight from them.

— ◊ —

We walked for an hour to Montfort Fort on Saturday. Two hours of moderate walking was required to return from the Montfort fortress. The climb up was steep and took place at a moderate pace. The area was a favorite place to visit every once in awhile. This was the first time we had been back since I got sick. It was difficult for me to make it at first. I was tired from the morning of working in the garden. My feeling was better after I went for a walk. While our village friends joined us, our children chose to stay at home as usual. It was a pleasant day, and the company was enjoyable. It was a pleasant experience that I managed to complete the walk without difficulty. It gave me the confidence I needed in my body. Although I felt some muscle tension, I believe that I didn't have to move my body for quite some time.

Passover night arrived, and along with it, another atrocious terrorist attack on a Netanya hotel. The attack was followed by another atrocious terror attack on a Haifa restaurant where we used to eat as a family. There were a few other attacks that followed, but the Israel Defense Forces (or the IDF) had already moved into Palestinian territory to eliminate the terrorist cells. The Hezbollah is constantly at the border of Israel's northern frontier. There is no light at the end. Due to the political environment, our sales were still low. Our financial obligations were very high and we could lose our company if we didn't sell. I prayed for a quick resolution to this difficult period.

— ◊ —

Rivka and me visited Dr. Keret yesterday. Each time I meet him, it stirs up my emotions. I couldn't remember so I asked him to show me the encyclopedia that had the seven requirements a patient must meet to survive. He said that I had fulfilled all of them, and therefore was likely to survive. Some of the requirements were: Making positive changes in the business, feeling happier, having a higher satisfaction level, and being more physically active. He gave me the task of finding other patients with prostate cancer who had survived or recovered long enough to be able to help them. This task was exciting to me. It was possible for others to recover, but Rivka and I talked on the road home. Rivka told me that I had no real chance of full recovery, based on everything we knew.

Yet, I felt great. I wore shorter pants which made it easier to walk and I found that I could easily climb up the stairs two at a stretch. I felt almost healthy, just as in the old days.

— ◊ —

My experience has shown that hormonal treatment can be stopped if the PSA drops below 0.05 for at least one year. This is to ensure that the hormone treatment does not cause cancer return and spread. One can live for many years with a hormonal treatment that is given at regular intervals. I talked to Dr. Rassan again about this possibility. I asked him what was bothering you about the treatment, but he refused to answer. Did it have to do with the fact that I could not have an erection. He was very insensitive to spiritual and physical aspects. I told him about the side effects of hormonal therapy for prostate cancer patients who had metastases. He replied that there was no protocol. His answer led me to two serious conclusions. It felt like a hammer hitting my head twice.

My first conclusion was that I needed to continue my hormonal treatment for the rest.

Second, I concluded that the hormone treatment would no longer be effective and the cancer would return. This would leave me at the mercy God or, to put it another way, my condition would worsen and nothing would work.

As I tried to get over this terrible news, I explained to the doctor that the most troubling thing about me was how to deal with the fact that the cancer recurred despite my hormonal treatment.

He did not answer me, he didn't have an answer.

My condition reminded me of a soldier who goes off to war and takes all his ammunition with him. He will likely need more ammunition in the future, but he is already out of his ammunition and is unable defend himself.

I was very conscious that doctors didn't have the right technique to deal with the cancer surge during hormonal treatment. I did not want to be surprised later, but I had to look for the techniques that would work for me.

Again, I had to learn the hard way that doctors were not people with a lot of knowledge and that they could not be trusted.

— ◊ —

Today, I went to Nahariya hospital to get my monthly Zomera dose. It was my first time Zomera had been funded by the health service and I was happy about it. I had printed the results of the most recent PSA test I took just a few days before I got there. My PSA score was disappointing. It was expected to fall further, but it held steady at 0.4. It appears that I am at the point where the hormonal treatment is about to lose its effectiveness and the PSA will begin to rise.

Nadir is the point at which PSA begins to rise from its lowest level. This is the turning point that is bad for the patient. It is the moment when the disease is returning to its original form. This is when the hormonal treatment for prostate cancer patients is not effective and the PSA levels rise despite treatment. It is known as HRPC (Hormone Resistant Prostate Cancer). Most cases of death occur at this stage.

Had my PSA level reached nadir? Although I believed it did not, my heart knew that there had been a shift in my condition. The hormonal treatment I was receiving stopped working six months after I started it.

I felt like I was in a scary stage of HRPC, which is something that oncologists don't really know how to manage.

When I returned home, I felt the urge to share with Rivka the events of that day. I suggested that she go on a walk. Outside our front door, I noticed a group of silkworms crawling in a straight line. It looked like a long, thin rope. This sight was utopia to me, unlike the storm that was raging within me.

Rivka heard about my day and the terrifying stage I was in. Rivka, in her own way, tried to convince my that it wasn't certain and that there were still options. I told her it was futile to try to convince me otherwise and that I did not want to cling to comforting words when I knew the truth. I said, "What I should now do is to learn from others' experiences how to cope with metastatic prostate cancer." This was also in line with the task assigned to me by my naturopath. I needed to find out about other people's coping strategies. At this stage, I had a goal.

—◇—

My good friend Lenny called that evening. Rivka was Rivka's coworker when we introduced him to a teacher at a nearby kibbutz. Lenny suggested that they meet at our home and she agreed to meet him there. We agreed. Lenny agreed to help me find the survivors I was looking for. Don Cooley's forum only dealt with advanced prostate cancer. Lenny helped me navigate the maze of the site.

It was an invaluable tool that I considered to be very useful. Being able to talk with others who have the same problems and offer support was a huge benefit. I was able to get real-time updates from the field about all the new inventions and problems. Lenny encouraged my decision to discontinue hormonal treatment, saying that it was only me (and not any doctor) who should decide. Robert Young, a man with prostate cancer and metastases was on the forum. He was diagnosed after his PSA exceeded 1,000. After undergoing hormonal treatment, he was placed on a break. Although his PSA was still high at 30 (about 30%), he decided to stop hormonal treatment when his PSA reached 80. I was also intrigued by his innovative Quadrament treatment. It intrigued me and I wanted to know more. The man was also an interesting person who created a glossary on prostate cancer terms that he published online (Phoenix5 - The prostate cancer glossary.

I read a lot, mostly online. The prostate cancer forum had the most current information about the latest treatments, and side effects. I also read many articles published online by doctors. The forum information was more useful than articles. The forum information was provided by the patient, the "end customer", and dealt with the product known as the "medical treatment." I understood the forum language because it was my own language. The patient described the treatment results in the forum, and I was able to clearly see what worked for him. If I had any questions, I could ask the patient and get an answer in a matter of minutes. Patients described in detail the side effects of the different treatments. When a patient spoke of fatigue from the treatment that forced him to stay in bed for the whole day or how he went out with his wife to eat properly, I was able to understand his meaning immediately.

However, most articles written by researchers and doctors discuss the results of a study or trial. The doctor who ran the trial usually wrote the article. His results were summarized statistically without noting any unusual cases. Knowing that statistics didn't give me much hope, and as a patient worried for my own health, I searched for the secret recipe to get me the deviation results I needed and keep me on the right track.

A doctor who writes articles does not address patients. He instead addresses an academic or professional authority. He expects to be acknowledged by some professional after his publication. Side effects are a crucial parameter for patients. It can be summarized in a few sentences such as "Among the participants, one or two had pulled out of the trial because of side effects." These side effects are often minor or manageable." I don't think all of this is helpful in helping me decide the best treatment.

Many articles end with a comment like "More work needed."

"To be done in that area." This sentence always makes me wonder. Do more work if it is necessary. Yes, there are always limits to time and funding. Reality dictates. Perhaps the writer isn't confident enough in his work to be able to defend himself against any incongruence with reality?

This is not meant to disparage the work of other researchers. I also realize that studies have helped humanity move forward, and that we all can attest to this. For my personal reasons, however, I found the forum to be more beneficial.

Retrospectively, I see that my participation in this forum and the knowledge that I gained there have had a tremendous impact on my success fighting the scum and saving me life.

Slowly, it became clear that I was in the midst of the most difficult battle of my entire life. I knew that I had to do everything I could to win. Although I knew the odds of winning, I was happy to accept a partial victory.

After my last meeting with Dr. Rassan I decided to complete a document that combined all our assets. Rivka would need to see a detailed report on the assets and undertakings of the dairy. Dror mentioned that we needed to make a contract in order to settle any differences between us, in the event of my death. It was a good thing he mentioned it on a night car ride, as I could not see his tears rolling down as he spoke.

Avivit was kind enough to invite me back. I wanted her to give me her thoughts on the various treatments that were available. Dr. Ruthie called me and informed her about my test results, Dr. Rassan's meeting with me, and how Avivit was interested in meeting me. Although she felt that Avivit was the best person to speak to, she insisted on meeting me. Although I was able to arrange the meeting with Avivit directly, I wanted Ruthie to be informed so that she understood the reasoning behind it. We agreed that she would arrange the meeting with Avivit. Ruthie seemed less interested in my case than I thought. I was not surprised that her energy for my case was very limited. I came back to the same conclusion repeatedly: only I could take care myself. This was true for me and any other problem. Relying on others is possible up to a certain point, but not blindly.

Lenny offered to help me locate people who had been there and done it for many years. I confided in Lenny about my desire for other options to treat my condition than the hormonal treatment. We asked Don Cooley a question about advanced prostate cancer (APC) and he replied. I posted a question asking for people with a similar condition as mine.

Two answers came back to me the next day. One was very interesting. Bill Aishman wrote it. I wondered if he was related Nazi murderer Adolphe Eichmann. But it wasn't relevant at the time. Even if I was aided by a nephew, or any other relative of the Satan personified, I had to keep my eyes on my own problems. Bill was also sick, but his was a worse condition. He suggested that I undergo chemotherapy simultaneously with the hormonal treatment to greatly increase my chance of survival. To support his arguments, he wrote a well-written article. This was his core argument:

The presence of testosterone can cause cancerous cells. These cells are known as AD (Androgen Dependent). The hormonal treatment can suppress these AD cells by reducing the body's testosterone production.

There are however, more dangerous cancer cells than those that have genetic mutations in the AD cells. These cells are known as AI (Androgen Independent), and their activity is not dependent on testosterone levels in the body. This means that hormonal treatments have no effect whatsoever. These cells cause the disease to spread and can even lead to death.

The group of male hormones called androgens includes testosterone.

The problem is that doctors don't know how to treat AI cell cancer. Therefore, they have no way to deal with the reactivation of the disease during hormonal treatment. Contrary to conventional medical treatments, chemotherapy can kill or suppress AI cells over a longer time period, allowing for a longer life expectancy. Side effects of chemotherapy are minimal and the recommended dose is low.

He gave many examples of patients who had survived for at least fifteen years. Another argument for chemotherapy is that breast cancer patients receive it right away after being diagnosed. Breast cancer is also a hormonal type of cancer.

Bill advised me to get chemotherapy right away and not wait because I was high-risk. He regretted not using this strategy as he didn't know about it at the time.

I felt a little hope in his sincere response, especially after Dr. Rassan had taken it away unintentionally. I decided to explore the possibility with top Israeli experts. I got to work.

Lenny was contacted by me to discuss the article. He was to meet the head of Haifa's oncology ward while accompanying another patient who was seriously ill for consultation. Lenny promised that he would ask the doctor about my condition and to offer him chemotherapy. Orna, our relative, was a nurse at another hospital's urology ward. I spoke with her and sent her the article. I asked her to contact Professor Niv, an Israeli oncologist who specializes in metastases and prostate cancer.

$$- \Diamond -$$

My support group met last night with the Haifa head of an erectile disorder clinic. Since I had other pressing issues to attend to, the meeting was a waste of time. We learned a lot about male sexual mechanisms and discussed the issues that various treatments can cause. The problem is that the male hormone testosterone is not produced. This causes the patient to lose his libido, or sexual drive. There is no other option. One can use Viagra or another similar drug to have sexual intercourse. However, it is not the same thing.

It is safe to say that testosterone alone does not make a person sexually potent.

The meeting was beneficial for me. Lenny and me consulted with the doctor at the end about chemotherapy. He was an oncologist, not a urologist.

The experts in the field of urology are specialists in the treatment and care of the reproductive system.

The experts in cancer are called oncologists.

The doctor agreed that our statements were rational and recommended Dr. Ace is a chemotherapy-specializing oncologist. His residency was with Dr. Ace was a US physician and Ace was the top-ranked expert in Israel on this topic. I called Dr. Ace left a voicemail on his home telephone.

I felt worse. Despite my low PSA, I started to feel pain in the pelvis while driving. I also felt shortness of breath, and new pain in my upper back. My back felt stiff, and it affected my movement. It was difficult for me to put on socks or tie my shoeslaces. These were psychological or physical manifestations. I was unsure.

— ◇ —

Avivit called to schedule an appointment. Just as I was feeling like the ground was shifting beneath me, Avivit's phone call came in just in time. Ruthie had met Ruthie a few days before and made arrangements for us to meet on Sunday. However, it was up to me to decide the time. She agreed to join us if we met at seven o'clock in the evening. Ruthie was a great support during my meetings with oncologists. I knew I could trust her professional background and she was there to help me when I needed it most.

Avivit thought my condition was great and joked about Dr. Rassan. I found it inappropriate and replied, "So, are Rassan irritating you?" She then asked me the details and I explained. She wanted to know if I had exercised. It was also my physical effort driving to Tel Aviv, running there, and working in the dairy that day. This was not too difficult, but it was physically demanding.

However, the alarming symptoms started the week before so this cannot be the cause. I asked her if there was anything more that could be done before Sunday. I was told to keep an eye on developments and she asked me when my last PSA was taken. She said it was April and that X-rays were unnecessary if the PSA was low. I informed her that I was interested in discussing chemotherapy. She agreed. We agreed to meet on Sunday afternoon at five in the evening. Although I regret not having Ruthie at the meeting, Rivka would be taking notes. She would then report back to me.

I was quite depressed. I felt like I was falling apart without anyone being there to stop me. In case I wasn't able to communicate my thoughts to them, I wrote a letter.

I entered my normal password to ensure that the documents were not made available before it was too late or for any reason not intended.

A will was also written for me.

— ◊ —

I felt guilty for not writing in a while. Although it is odd, I felt like I wasn't fulfilling my writing commitment. It bothered me, even though I couldn't explain it. In my defense, I will admit that it wasn't because of negligence. It was because of the series of events and problems that were weighing heavily on my shoulders. I put a lot of effort into the APC patient forum online.

Everything Bill Aishman wrote was read by me. He was one the most knowledgeable forum members. He encouraged patients to examine their illnesses down to the most basic details. He would sometimes scold patients for not being able to understand their illness and ask them questions that he felt were worthless or who he believed were not helping them get the right treatment. He proposed a theory that chemotherapy given to patients with prostate cancer who have metastases may improve their quality of life and longevity. This was something that no Israeli doctor had considered, and I don't believe any prostate cancer patient has ever received chemotherapy. I carefully read what he had to say. It seemed like there was a lot logic in his new arguments. This was the treatment strategy that I needed to follow?

These things confused me greatly.

One, I felt like my disease was resurfacing despite the hormonal treatment and the local hospital wasn't offering any other treatment. However, I was unsure if they would grant me chemotherapy. This is despite the fact that no one else in my situation has ever received it in Israel. There was no guarantee that the outcome would be the same as Bill's article?
My decision to undergo chemotherapy was the most risky I had ever taken in my entire life.

I sought advice from Dr. Ace and Avivit. Dr. Ace stated that there was no evidence to support the positive effects of chemotherapy administered simultaneously with hormonal treatment for prostate cancer patients who have metastases. He concluded that there is no evidence that chemotherapy prolongs or improves the quality life of prostate cancer patients who have metastases. Dr. Ace charged $385 for his consultation. It was indeed an Ace to charge such a large sum for just over an hour. I asked him for two receipts so that the HMO clinic could reimburse me for the majority of the cost. This is part of my right each quarter to consult an expert. He said, "No." He replied, "It messes with my accounting." I wrote him an entire check.

Avivit wanted to find out what Dr. Ace had told Avivit. I told her and she agreed. They both suggested that I take a small amount of the drug thalidomide. This drug stops the formation of blood vessels that supply blood to cancer cells. It also suppresses the growth of cancerous cells. Although the drug worked in mice, it has not been shown to be effective in humans. Dr. Avivit and Ace both reiterated this fact but stated that I had nothing to lose by trying it.

A large conference on prostate cancer was held in Haifa, Israel on Friday. Participants included top doctors as well as patients. Patients had questions answered by the doctors. I had a question about thalidomide. Although the answer was not positive, it was vague and I probably misunderstood my intent to use it simultaneously with hormonal treatment. The doctors warned me about possible side effects. I also emailed Dr. Charles Myers with my question, an American oncologist who specializes in prostate cancer. I planned to email Dr. Strom, an American specialist about the matter.

— ◊ —

It was horrible. It rose to 0.9. It was now a reality. The hormonal treatment did not work. I have reached Nadir and beyond. Although the increase in the PSA from the previous reading was only 0.5%, the fact that it had more than doubled in a month was very concerning. The PSA took less than a month for it to double, which indicates that a deadly illness is spreading rapidly. As my spirits fell into the abyss, I felt the sky falling on me. Did I feel like I was on a slippery slope and could not stop?

That week was hard work for me and I probably felt exhausted. Maybe that was another factor in my condition. I had to go back to work, but only a part of it. It would have me home at two in the morning instead of six in evening.

I thought about hiring a doctor to manage my illness and personally handle my treatment. At this point I had already consulted several doctors but none were willing to personally commit to me. Avivit was too busy and didn't have any strings attached. The same happened with Dr. Ace. I knew Dr. Rassan wouldn't lead me anywhere. Lenny suggested that I talk to Professor K at the Haifa hospital. He was a mansch and a top-rate professional. He was also unable to make it in time for me.

It was then that I realized I was my manager. It was up to me to take the realization in my head and implement it. I was the only one who could do it for me.

— ◊ —

Shavuot was a festival celebrating dairy products. People all over Israel would rush to buy large amounts of cheese. This was a great move for our company. It would be great if it was like this every day. My friend Lenny ran the shop when we reopened it. He exclaimed with excitement that all the cheese had been sold, and that there was no more for the next day. Naturally, he exaggerated a bit.

Shavuot was a very happy festival for dairy farmers.

CHAPTER SEVEN

THE CHEMOTHERAPY PROTOCOL

Late May 2002

These last few days have seen many developments. Yesterday morning I received my Zomera monthly dose. Although the treatment appeared to effectively suppress the growth of metastases it had side effects. After each treatment, I experienced pain in my bones for two days. It was similar to the flu. It could have been related to the hormonal treatment.

After my treatment, I had an evening meeting at the dairy where I met a potential client. At nine, I felt overwhelmed by extreme fatigue. I was dizzy when I returned home from work at half past ten. The dizziness continued the next day, and it was dragging me down. I took Orr to a Math help session before his Math matriculation. On the return trip, I was totally out of it. Midday came and I returned home to find an email from Larry Sorenson (an Australian patient) whose cancer was similar to mine. The results of his chemotherapy were very good. His PSA levels dropped significantly. He detailed all details about the treatment, including the protocol. He also had minor side effects. Larry seemed very happy with the treatment. This made me wonder if it would work for me.

Like other protocols, a chemotherapy protocol is a description of the treatment. It contains all necessary information for the treatment. This includes the type and dosages of the drugs and the complementary drugs. The length of each treatment and frequency.

I arrived at the dairy around two in the afternoon to meet with our accountant. During the meeting I felt like my energy was returning and I was slowly getting back to my former self. I realized it was due to side effects of Zomera, which encouraged me to try again. I returned home around five and assisted Bat-El in her physics homework.

I was so excited by the information that the Australian sent me, that I sent his email to Ruthie. I also spoke with her over the phone. She promised to review it and get back with me. The next step was to send the information and request their assistance for this treatment. Ruthie agreed that I should have another PSA test. She believed I was feeling depressed due to the emotional strain that the PSA increase had caused. On the other hand I was certain it was objective.

I took the PSA on the next day.

— ◊ —

There was so much going on that I couldn't keep up with it all. Although I did not want to miss anything, I was unsure if it would make any difference to anyone.

We met Dr. Ruby on Sunday night. He was a Haifa-based oncologist who I had previously been consulting. He was an expert in hormonal treatments. He was the host of the meeting. He was also interested in the information I had provided about the chemotherapy option. I gave him a copy of the material and promised to send him more details. Dr. Ruby is a kind, humble person. Our meeting lasted over an hour. He suggested that I try another line of hormonal therapy. He did however admit that the second-line treatment only lasted half as long as the first. I did the math. The first treatment lasted six month. Therefore, a second hormonal treatment would only last three months. Then there is the inevitable death and deterioration. It is not a positive outlook, I fear.

I didn't accept his proposal. I was determined to get chemotherapy.

I asked him how much he owed me at the end of our meeting. He said there was no charge. We were surprised when he replied that he accepted private patients, but that he didn't want to pay us any money. We promised him to send him goat cheese. We agreed to send him goat cheese, but he requested that it be small, as he and his wife live at home.

On Tuesday, Dr. Keret and I met again. The meeting was as usual interesting. The issue of convincing the institution to grant me the chemotherapy that I wanted was discussed. We used a very effective communication style to communicate our message to Dr. Bassam who I was due to meet Wednesday. I was concerned that he might offer alternative treatments that were less standardized by the medical establishment. I felt like I was going to war for this treatment when I left Dr. Keret.

We stopped at the clinic on our way back to get the most recent PSA test results. My worst fears were confirmed when the reading came back at me: it was 1.7. It felt like I was being pulled under the rug. Two weeks passed before the PSADT doubled in rate. This was because the increase in PSA and the resurgence cancer were both very rapid.

My future PSA was calculated if the PSADT remained at two weeks. My PSA could rise to 1,000 in five months. This PSA level often indicated an irreversible, total failure of the body's functions, and a life-threatening situation.

My neck was again encircled by the noose. Rivka looked shocked and helpless, even though there was nothing surprising. This day was coming. We knew the hormone treatment would end at some point. It was approaching, but suddenly it hit us with such a terrible intensity. Both of us went into shock as if it was something we hadn't prepared for.

I called Ruthie when I got back home to discuss the matter. It was obvious that I wasn't making this up and that it was frighteningly real. Avivit called shortly thereafter. Avivit called me shortly after I mentioned my PSA score. She said that she had read all of the material I sent to her and found it interesting. She said that she had changed her mind about my PSA score and decided to grant me chemotherapy according the Australian protocol. This was exactly what I requested. We agreed that she would write Dr. Bassam's evaluation and recommend that he give me the treatment. I felt victorious. I had broken through the glass ceiling. It was strange to feel happy that the system gave me chemotherapy as if it had given me a prize?

Larry Sorenson, an Australian, was my age and we were in the same stage. Our communication strengthened because I was involved in the treatment he received. His condition was very dark when he was diagnosed in 2001 with prostate cancer. His PSA was around 300, and he received a Gleason 9. This indicated that he had a malignancy level. (As previously mentioned, the highest level is 10 for malignancy. His entire body was affected by metastases. Larry, an extraordinary analytical man, didn't want to undergo the standard course hormonal treatments. He chose to undergo a combination of a chemotherapy protocol and a hormonal treatment. He had just finished his treatment and was showing rapid improvement when I reached out to him. His PSA dropped to almost zero, his bone metastases shrank, and it seemed that he was making progress. In his twenties, we discovered that he had been a volunteer at Kibbutz Kinerret in the Tiberias area. My former girlfriend and I had been spending a lot time at that kibbutz back then. We may even have bumped into one another. Larry sent me the chemotherapy protocol along with a graph showing how his PSA dropped after treatment. He also included a photo of his metastases prior to and after treatment. He was born in Australia and was treated at a Los Angeles clinic that specializes in prostate cancer. Dr. Leib, and Dr. Tuck were both Jewish doctors who ran the clinic. They offered unconventional treatment methods that were not supported by the medical establishment.

Larry's chemotherapy protocol included a combination of three chemo ingredients. Taxotere was the first component. It is also used in other chemotherapy protocols such as breast cancer and lung cancer. Although Taxotere is derived from the bark of a pine tree, Taxotere is synthesized in a laboratory. It kills cancer cells by disrupting their mitosis. Clinical trials have shown that this drug has an anticancer effect and prolongs the lives of patients with prostate cancer by up to three to four months.

Although prolonging the lives of patients by three to four more months may seem like a small achievement, it is a great news for some patients:

These are the statistical results from the trial. You have patients whose life was not extended by the drug; on the other hand, there are patients whose lives have been extended beyond what the statistical average.

This is also a significant accomplishment for researchers over the years.

Carboplatin was the second component of chemotherapy. It is part of the anti-neoplastic, platinum-based family of medications that are used in various chemo protocols.

Estramustine (Estracyt) was the third component. The ministry of Health approved this drug for patients with prostate cancer as a second-line treatment, meaning that it is used after the main treatment has ended.

The protocol also included aids like antinausea medication.

I found a few parameters that seemed to be logical about this protocol. It was not based only on one chemo component, but three. My logic said that they had to work together. They worked on different mechanisms so I assumed they would work together. The second reason I liked the frequency of treatment was that it was consistent. Patients are usually treated with chemotherapy once every three weeks. Larry's protocol states that chemotherapy was administered once per week at a third the usual three-weekly dose. This protocol was also known as "low-dose chemotherapy."

I found low-dose chemotherapy administered once per week to be more effective than triple doses every three weeks.

One of the things I saw in Sarona was a cat beating a large viper snake on the head. It happened during my childhood. This was what I called "The Way of the Cat". The cat beat the snake repeatedly on his head with many small blows until he finally gave up. This principle reminded me of the chemotherapy protocol Larry was getting: short, rapid blows to the scum until it was hopefully defeated. Patients were not used to receiving high-frequency treatments from doctors. This could be because of the congestion caused by weekly treatments in a already packed oncological ward.

In recent years, I learned that oncologists have created a new way to treat patients with cancer. This involves a series of aggressive treatments in the hospital followed by a period of rest for the body. Pill-based treatments allow the patient to take his daily dose at the home. This relieves the pressure on the already overcrowded oncology wards. These treatments aim to eliminate the need for intensive hospital treatment by ensuring that tumors are always targeted with low doses.

Another reason I supported this protocol was my fear of the severe side effects of high-dose treatments. Larry assured me that his side effects from treatment were minimal--no vomiting or hair loss. He felt more fatigued a few days after treatment.

It was time for a decision. It was an emotional decision, despite the logic behind this new treatment. Other than what I had learned through my forum "friends", and my intuitions, I didn't have much to go on. I wasn't sure which path was best for me. It was unlike any decision-making experience I have ever had before. It was like I was in thick fog and there were no signs to guide me. It felt like my life was at risk. I considered all the pros and cons and made a decision. There was no more hesitation. I wanted to follow the "Australian" protocol.

Next, I had to obtain Dr. Bassam's permission to implement this protocol. Three new points were worth mentioning. First, this was my first treatment with chemotherapy for prostate cancer. Second, my treatment was likely to be at the patient's own request. Third, I brought the protocol to the doctor rather than the doctor giving it to me.

I was not sure where this path would take me. All I knew was that this was the road I would be taking.

— ◊ —

I met Dr. Bassam on Wednesday afternoon at 1pm for the most important meeting of my life. I wanted to ask him for his approval of my chemotherapy protocol. I felt very tense. I wasn't sure if he would accept a treatment no one else in my situation had received. To my knowledge, I was also the first patient to choose his own protocol of treatment. Avivit's supporting letter was with me. Rivka arrived at the dairy to pick me up about 30 minutes before the meeting. We used the driving time for rehearsing my case convincingly so we could get Dr. Bassam's support and consent. Dror, my dairy business partner, had been treated by him when he was diagnosed with cancer twenty years ago. I began by telling him that I wanted him treating me the same way he treated Dror. He said he would try, but he didn't promise success. This funny opening made it easy to get along and make the rest of the conversation easier. I presented Avivit with the material and expressed my urgency to receive the protocol. I explained to him that while the treatment I had received up to then was effective, it wasn't as effective now, so I needed to devise a new plan.

We were surprised to find that he was willing to do it. Although it may seem trivial, you should realize that this was a novel, unconventional protocol that was being presented for the first time. I was required to obtain Taxotere privately from the Ministry of Health, as the doctor had to get approval. This was a costly step that would have financial consequences of close to $3,000 per monthly. I advised him to not worry about the cost of the drug but the medical aspects of the treatment. Dr. Bassam also consulted Avivit during the meeting. After I took the drug and found it effective, she told Dr. Bassam that it could be funded by Ministry of Health.

We agreed to start the treatment on the following day because of the urgency that I displayed during the meeting. I needed to find the drug the same night. I was acquainted with a woman whose partner died from cancer. She was given Taxotere, and she still had some doses that she would be willing to give to any person in need. She only requested a letter from Dr. Bassam, my oncologist. Bassam--indicating that I required the drug. As my oncologist was filling in forms for the treatment I called the woman to confirm that we could get the drug from her. She told me that she could meet us at her home at eight in the evening.

With an odd feeling of relief and ease, we drove to her. My chemotherapy protocol was approved and I was thrilled. While I felt I had overcome a major hurdle, I was also anxious about the treatment. I had no idea what the outcome would be. What side effects would I experience? Yet, I was happy to have won another battle.

I called my dad and informed him that I would be starting chemotherapy the following day. I was certain he would share the news with the rest of my family. It was only a short conversation. He didn't ask any questions about the treatment. This was unusual for him. He was hardened by the treatment, as if he had been given a horrible verdict that he could not defend. He thanked me for the update, and I was moved to tears by his words.

We drove together to pick up my first dose of "poison". A beautiful woman came up to us with a tragic story. She was an eleven-year-old woman who had fled England to work as a marketing director at a small, but successful electronics company. Slowly, she developed a romantic relationship and decided to marry the director and owner of the company. The guy was suffering from prostate cancer for many years and was being monitored. Despite all the care and monitoring he received, terminal prostate cancer took hold and spread to his liver and other vital organs. He died soon after. He was without a leader, engineer or woman and left the company. She said that she had heard about his illness before they got married. She sat down with me for nearly an hour and a quarter, and she shared her thoughts over coffee and cake. We agreed to stay in touch after we had finished with the drug. Rivka and I were driving home when Rivka told me, "They couldn't even have proper sexual sex, those poor people."

We went to the clinic the next day to obtain paperwork and another drug to start the chemotherapy protocol. In the hope that it would stop my unruly cancer from spreading, I started to get my poison three times per month.

I traveled a new and difficult road with great hope.

CHAPTER EIGHT

THE CHEMOTHERAPY TREATMENT

Late May to Late September 2002

Normal people think of chemotherapy as a difficult treatment that involves vomiting, hair loss, severe weakness, and other unpleasant side effects. Before I began treatment, I felt the same. However, most of these did not occur or were only partially realized. Other things did happen, however.

I was at the oncological unit again. Because of my Zomera treatment, everyone knew me. Because of my unique story, and the way I handled it, I felt special attention. It was almost as if I was a celebrity being greeted by nurses and staff. It helped me to relax before my first chemotherapy treatment.

Two bags of chemotherapy drugs were in my treatment program. The other bag contained cleansing water. My total treatment program was three liters. The nurse placed the needle in my vein. The nurse began by cleaning my vein with sterile water. After that, the drugs started to trickle into me. It took quite a while. It took me three hours to complete the treatment. There was another hour of bureaucracy that added an additional hour, making it slow and depressing. Surprisingly, I felt fine. It might not be as bad as I thought.

Because I knew I would read, I took two books. Rivka received one book as a gift. On a 2000 summer trip, I had already read another book by the author. We sailed through the English Channel on a chartered vessel. The cruise lasted approximately a week and I read the entire book. It was a passionate, fascinating love story about a Jerusalem woman at the beginning of the 20th century. Orr, my son, devoured the book as well. My teenager shared my enthusiasm and enjoyed the book. I was proud. He enjoyed analyzing the plot with me, but I tried to avoid enticing him into discussing lustful descriptions.

I started to read the book but couldn't concentrate. I spent the time staring at space and learning new features from the mobile phone that I was upgraded to by my cellular company. I was amazed at the speed and variety of technology available. I fell asleep for a portion of the time, drifting off to fragmented, semi-sleep. The poison remained in my body for the entire time. I didn't feel any discomfort, other than the needle being inserted into my vein. As she did for the other patients, Nurse Ann was attentive to my needs, changing bags as needed, and ensuring that I was well taken care of.

It was amazing to me how people could take on the job of caring for patients with horrible illnesses every day and still manage to do their jobs with grace. If I had been in this field, I don't think I would have made it long.

After four hours of chemotherapy, they finally unhooked my needle. Rivka called me to pick up my treatment. She gave me instructions on how to swallow the many pills that day. I said goodbye to Ann and the other staff members as I left.

I felt like a prisoner, being released from jail after leaving the building. I felt like a prisoner being released from prison. The warmth of the sun and the freedom to do anything I wanted gave me an energy boost that can only be experienced by those who have been hooked up to IVs for more than three hours. Orr and Rivka waited for me in my parking lot. Although they looked at me with some concern, I smiled at them and continued walking steadily.

I fell asleep at home after being overcome with fatigue. My sweet sleep was a natural reaction to the exhausting treatment. My brother Arieh called me in the afternoon to check on my condition. I could hear his concern. I tried to disarm it with humor. He offered to come and visit me in the evening, which I happily accepted.

Arieh arrived at the house late as usual. We were the only ones in the house. Rivka went to school along with the children, while Dina went shopping with Sharon, her future bride, for a wedding gown. We had some quality time together, just the two of them, and we chatted about various topics and about me. My illness seemed to be a hot topic that day. Although it was comforting to be the center of attention, I worried about how it would affect my ability to fully enlist my spirit in my recovery. This was a trap I couldn't afford to fall into.

I began to prepare dinner and pulled out the refrigerator contents, but I was feeling rusty. I think I was a little rusty in this area, and I didn't know how to properly arrange a dinner table. Rivka came shortly after and took care dinner. Arieh returned home after we had enjoyed a delicious meal.

— ◊ —

After chemotherapy, I rested for the weekend at home. I returned to the dairy on Sunday. After not being there for a while, I felt detached and even strange. It was as if my main focus had shifted to fighting my scum. Sometimes, I felt like I should just take a step back and concentrate on my health issues. However, I realized that if I stopped eating dairy, my obsession with the illness would be my main focus and would not help my mental health.

Dror was not happy with the situation. He felt strained by my absence from work. He said he was ready to fall. I believed him. This was a terrible thing for the dairy. I didn't know how much work I would be able to do during treatment. What if I could do more than what I was doing now? Dror suggested Dror hire another worker to help him at his dairy. However, no final decision was reached.

Thursday just before midnight. Today was my second chemotherapy treatment. After returning home, I had lunch and then went to bed. After that, I felt refueled, full of a positive load that had been filling me with interest and satisfaction, in direct contradiction to my physical condition and the tangible threat that was looming over my head.

Rivka and I discussed it during yesterday's walk. Rivka suggested that I shouldn't succumb to self-absorption as if I were the center and only thing that made the universe spin. Rivka believed that people around me didn't have to be there for my needs 24/7. Rivka told me about a colleague at work who lost her adopted daughter to cancer. She sometimes struggled to bear the emotional and physical toll of caring for her child. The child refused to go to chemotherapy when her mother drove her daughter to the hospital a few hours away. The mother, a senior teacher, was in danger of having a nervous breakdown. The mother, a senior educator, tried to explain to the social worker that she had to be compassionate towards the child. However, she said that she was an educator who knew exactly what she should do. She couldn't take any more pressure.

Rivka understood my point. We, as patients, need more attention and consideration. I feel so comfortable and at ease receiving this much attention, I'm almost in love with my situation. It is wonderful, but I worry that it is reducing my ability to fight the disease.

It was clear that I had to be more conscious of the impact my illness was having on those around me and do what I could to reduce it. It was not an easy task. My mind was always preoccupied with the disease and I was constantly tense. If I didn't release some of that tension, my body would have exploded. Like most things, I had to find balance. I didn't want to overburden my family and I also needed to release the tension that I felt.

People who are near death and have nothing to do, often wish for their loved ones to "over" it. This is not because they lack love for the dying but because the emotional burden that the illness places on their family becomes too much. This was the saddest thing that happened to my mother. Although I loved her deeply, it was difficult for me and everyone else to deal with her final moments. It was difficult to talk to her about meaningful things. The entire chapter in Cancer as a Turning Point (which I have already mentioned), is dedicated to communication with someone close to you. Author suggests having a "final talk" with the person to discuss the most important experiences and things in his life. Also, the "legacy" that he leaves behind. This will allow the dying person to have closure and acceptance.

Strangely, I felt that this finality didn't concern me. These topics have become less important to me over time. My soul has developed a suppression mechanism. This mechanism is actually common to all of us, as we all move in the same direction towards the inevitable end. Yet, we don't feel threatened or worried by it at all. It is quite normal, I suppose.

I suggested that Izhar make a film about my fight with cancer. Irit, his partner, was not too busy. They would love the idea, I think. Technically, he had a state-of the-art, new video camera. Both are media professionals. Irit is in production and editing and Izhar is in investigative journalism. Both were capable.

Irit, Izhar and I spent Saturday with us filming footage for a movie. Although I wasn't sure where it would take me, it was very enjoyable to be the focal point of attention once more. Rivka and I had a great conversation, which made me feel a bit guilty. Izhar received my journal as background research for the movie. This was the amazing reply I received the next day:

Isaac my brother,

Tonight, I finished most of the journal. Listen; I'm speechless.

It is incredibly powerful and moving. It's amazing to think that I didn't really know my brother until today.

We will continue to discuss. This is all I wanted to say for now. Keep writing.

Your brother

It was a wonderful way to end the day! It was 2:20 in the morning. Time to go to bed.

More writing tomorrow.

— ◊ —

Izhar, and Irit signed up quickly for the film project. They were there with us for the weekend. On Friday, they filmed and interviewed me in detail at home. Then, on Saturday, we went to Teva Ez where Lenny, our brother-in-arms was working our taverna. They also interviewed him. Lenny is known for his sincerity and unwavering honesty. He will tell anyone about his prostate problems or his sex life without any filters. He is also a fantastic storyteller and this added color to the movie. They decided to continue interviewing him at Haifa.

Yesterday, Izhar was with me during my hospital chemotherapy. He arrived on the train and I picked him up from the station to take him to the ward. I had to have prior approval before we could film him during treatment. It was great to have him there. We found out that Izhar only had one video cassette with them during filming. Rivka was asked to buy more cassettes. We discovered that Rivka had actually brought cassette head cleaners with her when she returned. She drove back to Nahariya, but I was nearly done with the treatment by the time she returned, so the tapes were not used much. We dropped Izhar off at the train station after the treatment.

— ◊ —

I visited a "sorceress" from a nearby village in an effort to heal. She used energy work and guided imagery with many sophisticated tools such as cards, cards, and a pendulum. She claimed that she received many energetic messages about me, my soul and other corners. When she was not connected to them, she sealed them like doors. She explained that the pendulum revolved in a circular motion when she was connected with my soul. When she wasn't, it would turn in a linear direction. Whatever.

The "sorceress", as she was called, had a colorful personality. She also said that she treated animals in her last session. Her daughter owned an equestrian farm in France that was used for competition horseback riding. She traveled there twice a year to visit the horses. When I asked how the horse responded, she shared a story about how she used Reiki to help a depressed horse. The session began when she placed the horse's head on the shoulder. A few minutes later she felt the whole weight of the horse's head on the shoulder. She looked at the horse and saw that he had fallen asleep like a baby in its mother's arms. I played with her and told her about my brother Arieh and the goat cheese that we made. She was excited and began to describe the region where her daughter lived, in central France's Loire Valley, which is home to excellent goat cheese. Many limestone caves are suitable for making cheese due to their high humidity and stable temperature. This is also why cheese production has grown so quickly over the years. As I was about to leave, she surprised and invited me to join her for her trip to France, which was only two weeks away. I explained my limitations and said that it wasn't something I thought would work.

She asked me, "Is it because you are supposed receive chemotherapy treatment?".

Her intuition was astonishing. I was curious to learn how she knew the treatment because I had never told her. Instead of answering, she smiled at her sorceress's smile as she shrugged.

Rivka was also present when I returned home.

She said, "Maybe you should leave.".

It seemed impossible, even though I thought it through again. I didn't have the energy or motivation to make this trip. What if my condition deteriorated? There were also treatments I needed to finish. Ruthie was as practical as ever and suggested that I bring Rivka along. She said that they could easily change the dates for me to make it work, as I would be away between seven and ten days. It was something I considered for a while and then it struck me. Rivka got excited when I spoke with her again. I decided to speak to Rivka again the next Tuesday to see what happened.

$$- \Diamond -$$

June was just beginning, and the hot summer days when you wanted to hide from the heat were upon us. The Ben-Ami village was much more humid than Mitzpe Hila. Your brain was fried as soon as you left the office, which wasn't pleasant. The dairy structure was isolated so you could spend time there on such days.

I felt the need to meet my school friends at Acre's naval officers' boarding schools. These were people I had met for the first time thirty-five years. Did I want to say goodbye? I didn't know. It was something I discussed with my Naturopath. He encouraged me to meet them. After not seeing me in a while, my friends came over to see me on Saturday. It was initially tempting to relax on the northwestern porch but the heat forced us into the air-conditioned living area. We enjoyed the food and wine, and had a lot of fun. However, there was very little intimacy. It was pleasant, but it wasn't heartfelt. I was at a point in my life where I realized that any social gathering without deep conversations about the real concerns of us was just a random gathering. This contrasted with my fascinating session with Izhar on Saturday, which gave me an opportunity to share what I was concerned about. To be able to apply the theory to others, I needed to let them talk about their concerns. There are a few essential elements that must be present, including a friendly atmosphere that encourages attentiveness and a keen interest in the topic under discussion.

— ◇ —

These past days have been slow. It has been oppressive heat. There was nothing exciting. I suppose I was used to being overwhelmed with recent events. I was again experiencing pain from the metastasis to my right pelvis. It couldn't leave me alone?

Avivit advised me to stop taking the Casodex.

The PSA is an indication that cancer cells are multiplying when the patient is taking Casodex. Casodex is used as a nutrient by cancer cells devoid of testosterone. The drug that had previously served to suppress cancer has now changed its course and is accelerating the spread of the disease. Unbelievable. It is a bizarre process that defies common sense.

It was also something I did online. Avivit was correct. It was a blessing to have her beside me. I was not told that by any other doctor.

My Zoladex shot which lowers testosterone production, was delayed ten days. It was required that I take it once every 12 weeks. I received it only after 13 and a quarter weeks. Could it have been that my testosterone levels had increased, and the PSA was on an alarming rise? It urged me to start the chemotherapy I was hoping would stop the spread of the disease, but on one side, the pain in my right pelvis returned. Is the pain due to not getting the shot on the right time? I hoped so.

Despite my thoughts and feelings, I took a good afternoon nap. The illness can cause a lot of mental stress. I was always preoccupied with thoughts that I couldn't let go of. The chemotherapy had not been effective enough for me in the last few days. I felt like the cancer was still alive and well despite all the chemotherapy. These sensations were very frightening, as any negligence or lack thereof could have a significant impact on the quality and length of my life. That afternoon, Dr. Ruby called and I was very happy.

He was an angel. He responded to a question I had faxed him several days before. I used the chance to ask him additional questions. He answered my queries patiently and in great detail. He said that chemotherapy is only effective after two months. It would be difficult to evaluate its effectiveness before that time. The PSA reading can be used to determine whether the treatment is working. He advised me to see a urologist to have a follow up and a test for testosterone. He was a calm and understanding person who helped me put things into perspective.

Today, a businessman called me to discuss a Polish cheese production company. He had lived in Poland for 11 years and claimed to be well-connected to all those who are involved in Polish business. He claimed that he had brought samples of Israeli cheese to important parties in Poland, and that they enjoyed them. He wanted to set up a subsidiary to produce and market these products throughout Poland. I was able to hear his plans and skills over the phone and he asked for a meeting in Tel Aviv with other parties to discuss all of the possibilities. Throughout the conversation, it was difficult to stop wondering if I was still in the game. Although I wanted to keep this "game of life," I was weak from chemotherapy and uncertain where it would lead. Uncertainty can make you crazy. I was unable to predict the future. Even the most basic things. Rivka felt my distress. Rivka suggested that we take a vacation and gave me a list from her board of education of places to visit. I didn't know how to answer. She suggested that I go to the theatre the next night. I didn't know how to answer this one. The chemotherapy made me feel weak, both emotionally and physically. Sunday was my hardest day. I felt the most tired three days later. Tomorrow should go a bit better.

— ◊ —

I received an email message from a patient suffering from advanced-stage cancer. The bone, brain, and lungs had all metastasized. We both assumed that he wouldn't survive long. He asked the patients' forum for any other suggestions. He was unable to have any more extensive treatments due to his low red blood count. He was offered thalidomide by his doctors, which was supposed slow down the development new blood vessels. Also, tranquilizers were recommended. I told him about a bone marrow transplant that I had heard of from a relative. The Swedish doctor who performed the treatment on one of his patients was interested in it as an experiment. The patient seemed to experience a dramatic improvement in his condition. This was all I could offer.

Apart from his depressing state, there were a few commonalities between us. He was also diagnosed at forty-nine. He had metastases in his pelvis and lung. He was treated with Aredia, an older drug that is less effective than Zomera. He had problems with his veins so he stopped taking Aredia. Although I hoped that I wasn't following his lead, who knows?

$$- \Diamond -$$

Rivka was forty-four today. I bought her a set of pampering beauty products that cost more than $100. These things are always too expensive for me. The salesperson wrapped it beautifully and I wrote a card wishing her a happy birthday and expressing my love. It didn't seem to have any effect on anyone. We were suggested to go out by her, but I was not up for it. We decided to go to a restaurant together the next day. We always had a great time with them at the Chinese restaurant in Nahariya on their birthdays.

$$- \Diamond -$$

The email that I received the previous day reached me. I felt like I was following the same path and the metastases were growing into my stomach all night. Ruthie called me the next morning to check on her. I left a message for Ruthie, but she did not answer. Next, I called the hospital's oncological ward. Mimi, the chief nurse, answered. I wanted to meet Dr. Bassam, or Dr. Rassan. Mimi replied, "Bassam isn't at the hospital today." She tried to calm my nerves and suggested that my symptoms could be side effects of chemotherapy. When I said that I didn't have anyone to count on, I was quite assertive. We agreed to speak with Dr. Rassan, and I would be there in the afternoon.

Mimi did not reassure me so I called Avivit. I did not get a response. I also left a voicemail. I was contacted by her shortly thereafter. She seemed tired and more exhausted than ever. I shared my feelings with her. It was not how metastases spread normally, she said. She suggested that I have a stomach sonogram to check for side effects of chemotherapy. She was able to calm me down. She was able to organize things when others had left me confused. I asked her why she was so tired, as the day had just begun. She replied that she didn't have enough time.

I called to schedule a sonogram appointment. In two weeks, I received an appointment. They said that "By the time salvation comes the soul will have perished." So I asked them for a later date. They placed me on the waiting-list. I was done with my scum and started work.

— ◊ —

Izhar, Irit and Irit visited us last Friday. We drove to Sarona on Saturday. They shot a few more segments along with me on the way. Since it was just the three of us, I allowed myself to get carried away. I talked about how precious time was becoming and how every day that I felt good was a gift.

I also talked about how I needed to write about what I could and should do in my life, as well as the things that I would most likely not do, and what I have accomplished in my life. I'd love to create a similar list one day.

We stopped at the Druze village Rama to take in the amazing view of the valley. Many times I dreamed of building a cable car that would take us from the valley to Carmiel. A Jungfrau in Switzerland, an amazing tourist attraction with lots of snow and many restaurants. In 1978, I was able to visit it. Izhar, Irit and Irit captured the scene of our long-lost childhood when we reached Sarona. We felt surrounded by a surge of nostalgia in a profound way.

Yesterday was the start of my third round in weekly chemotherapy. The chemotherapy was combined with the Zomera treatment. I was gradually getting into a routine, with three weekly treatments followed by a week of rest. Side effects that I was worried about weren't too bad. Although I did experience fatigue the third day following each treatment, it was not the worst. A dominant metal taste lingered in my mouth, which flavored all the food I ate. I still felt discomfort in my buttocks. Aside from all of that, and possibly due to my fear that the chemotherapy would fail, I was concerned that a two week break from chemo might allow the cancer to return.

I asked Dr. Bassam whether postponing Zomera treatment for 10 days had resulted in any damage. This drug is used to treat bone metastases and prevent them from breaking.

He replied, "It has not yet been proven as a treatment that can prolong the life of a person.".

"And what if that's all it does is prevent the horrible pain of fractures?" I insisted.

I felt that none of my doctors were able to tell me if the current treatments I was receiving were the best for me. They failed to meet my needs despite all their experience, knowledge, and goodwill. They couldn't really help me long-term. They didn't have the time to help you. It was evident that they did not care about you. The more you remained passive and asked less, the better you were at being a patient. This topic was also addressed in the book Cancer as a turning point, which analyzed this issue and discussed it extensively. Dr. Lawrance L. LeShan was naturally sympathetic to the active patient. He asks questions and expects answers. And he participates in the treatment decisions.

— ◊ —

In our family, a series of events was unfolding. Orr was having a graduation party at school, which happened on Thursday, my chemotherapy day. I was worried that I wouldn't be able make it. He was then scheduled to travel to England for three weeks as a counselor for the "Habonim Dror," a Jewish youth movement.

Arieh and Dina returned from London for two weeks on Saturday. Dina celebrated her fiftieth Birthday.

"Welcome, to the club of long-living," I congratulated.

Their daughter Shlomit, who had been on a long journey to the Far East, returned home from Thailand two days later. Two weeks later, Yoav was married to Sharon. My chemo coincided with their wedding. I hoped that I would be strong enough for them to celebrate.

Two questions about the efficacy of my chemotherapy and the options available to me came from me. I reached out to the forum. Bill Aishman sent me two articles. He was probably a scientist and full of ideas and knowledge. His first article covered the different chemotherapies, while his second article presented an innovative way to approach the treatment.

He said that doctors will continue to use a treatment until they are satisfied with its effectiveness. This can lead to new, more resistant mutations in the cancer. Bill recommended that treatment be stopped as soon as it is still effective and before new mutations can develop. He also suggested switching to a different course of treatment. This would allow one to resume an interrupted treatment after a time, and theoretically extend treatments indefinitely. This was a novel idea that challenged the accepted methods, and it provided us with some good news. His idea was very appealing to me--a deliberate interruption to the treatment. It sounded revolutionary.

Is it right for me? Do I want to adopt it? It is something I need to consider.

Today, I had to go through chemotherapy. I was exhausted. Orr was graduating that night. Rivka's parents came to the ceremony with her. Due to fatigue, I didn't go. Bat-El was already in Jerusalem, and Amir didn't want to go. Orr had never been to Orr's party. It was a shame that Rivka, from our nucleus, did not go. I spoke to Orr about it, and tried to meet him at the airport to catch him on his way to England. In my current condition, I knew that I couldn't promise anything. It is what it was.

— ◊ —

Friday night at midnight. Rivka and I had gone on a walk earlier in the day. We sat outside for quite a while. Rivka got tired so she went to bed. I came in to join her and my computer.

I've been meaning to write about what I have done, what I haven't accomplished and what I might do in my life. Midnight seemed the ideal time to start:

Things I have accomplished	Things I will probably accomplish	Things I probably will not live to accomplish
Became a family man	Send off Orr to the IDF	Attend any of my children's weddings
Became a homeowner	Celebrate Orr's release from the IDF	Become a grandfather
Became an engineer	Attend Bat-El's high school graduation	Become wealthy
Became a business owner	Watch Amir join his soccer team next season	Make Teva Ez profitable
Expanded the dairy	Make Teva Ez a better business	Have sex like I used to
Got settled financially		Own a Harely Davidson and travel with it
I found peace in all aspects of my life		

The table was a visual representation of my life. I was stunned to see the rows and columns that contained my thoughts, actions, and dreams. Some of these would never become a reality. Although I would add another column and name it "Dreams", it would only contain one cell:

"Recover against all odds."

— ◊ —

The last two days were spent writing Avivit a letter. I was so concerned that my treatments were not suppressing the disease as I expected. I tried to write the questions I was dreading as clear as possible. These questions were not answered by her or anyone else, which I knew. My creativity and knowledge enabled me to make my own suggestions for improving treatment methods. I sent her several articles and information about online treatment methods. Bill Aishman wrote an article about the deliberate interruption of chemotherapy.

I thought his idea was brilliant and original. He wanted to receive each treatment only for a short time and then move on to the next one before any mutations could develop. The patient can then experience all possible treatments, and revisit them in a cyclical fashion. This is similar to a soldier going into battle carrying a set amount of bullets, ammunition, and grenades. The uninformed soldier will use all of his ammunition in his rifle, followed by all of the grenades and then the secondary ammunition. However, the skilled soldier will only use some of the bullets and, only when necessary, the grenades or other ammunition. He will use his rifle bullets again later, if necessary.

It made me wonder what Avivit thought of it, and if it was practical.

Avivit was a Jewish-American researcher Steven A. Rosenberg. He is a pioneer in the field of cancer treatments. I purchased Avivit The Transformed Cell. It describes how cells are taken from a patient and genetically transformed to become immunization mechanisms against cancer. Although this method is not recommended for prostate cancer patients, it has moved me to tears.

— ◊ —

Ruthie and I had a hard conversation last Sunday. I was feeling very depressed and the tingling in my buttocks that had started recently made it even worse. It felt like the scum was taking control of that entire part of my body, and it was bringing me down. Ruthie had been very busy because her partner was out of town, so I gave all my problems to her. It was clear that she took it all very seriously.

— ◊ —

Avivit received my mail and called me back. I had left a voicemail message. She spoke with confidence and a familiar demeanor that "leave the professionals" and assured me that I was getting the right treatment. My current protocol was the best at the moment. She said that Bill was not an oncologist, and didn't know everything.

She said that the next treatment plan would be decided based on the individual situation and not planned ahead. Overall, it was pleasant and we did not change our treatment approach.

Ruthie and I spoke again the next day. I shared with Ruthie about Avivit's conversation and how my PSA had increased to 0.37. I felt quite good. Ruthie said that my mood was changing based on my test results. I disagreed. My mood changed based on my physical condition, which was also reflected in my test results. She suggested that I treat myself and my family to lift my mood and restore my vitality. This idea sounded good to me. I was thinking of taking my family on a short vacation abroad for a few days. Rivka suggested that we choose a place with cool climate. To avoid heat and humidity, I devised a creative solution: travel to Turkey's mountains.

Ruthie received a copy The Transformed Cell. I dedicated it to her as a gift from my "toughest patient" and thanked her for her support.

— ◊ —

Today, I received a very sad email. Don Cooley is the forum administrator and one the most active patients on the forum. He wrote it to respond to an email from another patient in which he expressed hope for a miracle cure for the suffering we all endured. Don explained that his wife was diagnosed at thirty-five with breast cancer. The doctors advised her to live for five years before she could be considered healthy. After eight years of battle, she died. Don also had terminal cancer.

— ◊ —

Arieh, my older brother came to visit me today at Teva Ez. We had lunch at Nahariya's regular hummus place. We talked and ignored the main issue that was weighing heavily on our souls. I couldn't hold it together on the return trip to the village. I felt like I was losing my mind. Although I wasn't sure he was ready, he quickly recovered and said that no one wanted it on him. I knew I wouldn't have much to live on after chemotherapy ended. I could only survive for so long on chemotherapy. This thought kept me awake at night and I couldn't let it go.

The night sweating I felt in my upper body began to return, reminding me of the condition that I had before being diagnosed. It was not only uncomfortable, but I was concerned that it might be an indication of disease progression. It was urgently needed.

A meeting was scheduled for Friday with the naturopath. I wanted to know how he could relieve the stress. I also wanted to talk with him about other topics. One person had his medical treatment stopped and he started taking lycopene (10 mgs per day) and saw palmetto (3300mgs three times per day). His condition improved dramatically. It seemed like there was some truth to the story and I wanted to know his thoughts. The article stated that the PSA of the man had fallen from 365 to 6 in a year and half. This was after all other treatments including chemotherapy.

Orna, our cousin who works in a urological unit, suggested a homeopathic doctor. He had done miracles for a friend who was fighting breast cancer. I promised to contact him as well, so he would be able to help me.

— ◊ —

We had a second meeting with Dr. Ruby. We were asked to determine how long I should continue my chemotherapy. This doctor was a man I admired greatly. Before giving his opinion, he took the time to study the case and review all medical records and images. Dr. Bassam was very different from him. He never looked at my CT images nor any other documents that were not in my medical files.

Dr. Ruby suggested six months of chemotherapy with a break in between. This seemed reasonable to me after I read the Australian protocol, which recommended six rounds of treatment. It was almost the exact same thing. This allowed me to continue with chemo for four more rounds until December. He also suggested taking lycopene. One of his patients had a one-year-long remission thanks to lycopene.

I thought to myself, "He takes pride in his patient living an entire year without any treatment other than taking lycopene." It is strange that a healthy person can live for one year without gaining any weight. However, for those with uncertain futures, a year feels like forever.

Lycopene, a red pigment found in tomatoes, is also found in other red vegetables. It has been shown to be anti-cancer, particularly against prostate cancer. Lycopene can be taken in capsules daily. Israeli scientist is believed to have isolated lycopene.

A new study claims that lycopene does not have any anti-cancer properties against prostate cancer. After years of taking lycopene daily, this study made me stop. I now take one less capsule per day. It's not bad.

In the days that followed, my spirits were somewhat lifted. My main reason for feeling better was my physical health. The second reason was an email from an Australian friend who sent me lots of helpful information. After completing fifteen cycles of chemotherapy, he was now on a break. Contrary to Israeli doctors, he decided to interrupt the chemotherapy. Dr. Bassam answered my question about how long chemo treatments would be effective. He said, "As long they work." However, I was still unsure if it made sense to keep the treatment going for so long, given the fact that the disease can develop resistance to treatment. He smiled and stated that he had been treating a patient for over a year. I assumed he would continue with my chemotherapy as long as it worked. It was better to think ahead than assume. I realized that he was going to "kill me softly", as Roberta Flack would say.

I felt that there wasn't any creative thought about how to beat this horrible disease. I also felt that I was being guided down the same path as those who died before me.

This is how does the system reduce the overcrowding of patients on the oncological wards?

Perhaps everyone was tired of my questions and my unanswered recommendations.

I was expecting to get clear information, but no one gave it. Every doctor has hundreds of patients, each one a separate world. Itzy Be'er is the most important person in their lives?

I thought back to the strategic decision that I made to end the chemotherapy protocol before the positive effects waned.

We drove Orr to the airport in order to take him to England. We stopped at a party to drop off Bat El on the way. We rented a room in a guesthouse on a kibbutz near the airport. This was where Rivka's family, the Dormans, lived. They provided free board and even invited us to dinner at their home, despite my protests. Ora, the wife prepared a delicious meal that was mindful of my dietary requirements. Amazing hospitality, no doubt. The problem was that my husband would not stop talking! We gave up when he was exhausted.

We slept in a small, cramped kibbutz, far from what we would consider a guesthouse. We woke at two in the morning and got dressed. Then we drove fifteen minutes to the airport. We gave Orr hugs and kisses as a goodbye, but it was too much. The chick felt like a bird, and flew its own way. Later that day, we felt even more anxious as he called us to confirm he arrived safely in London. He asked that we not call him so often that it wouldn't seem like we were protecting him. It was strange. On the one hand it was time for him fly and on the other it felt strange that we didn't want to be there with him, as though he was embarrassed by our presence.

We returned to the "guesthouse" at about five in morning. It was still dark and we were up until nine. We put the beds together and fell asleep. Despite my hormonal condition I felt the need to have sex. Rivka also wanted it. After a lot of fumbling around, I finally got to know Rivka. My hormonal treatment did not allow me to have decent sexual sex. It was awful. A high testosterone level is dangerous as it can spread the cancer. If a patient such as myself has sexual potential, it is nice but also indicates that he has a high testosterone level, which is very risky. We had a wonderful time of intimacy and she may have even come. After that, we fell asleep briefly. The cleaner knocked on our doors at eight to wake us up, despite the fact that the room was available until nine. We were upset, but couldn't help but to act. After getting up, we went to get breakfast with the Dormans.

We met again with the naturopath. I spoke with him about my fears regarding the nature of my treatment and how no one was managing my cancer project. Recent articles supported my concerns that the people who were taking care of my health were not keeping up with my needs and putting my life at risk. I found Dr. Bassam's assertion that chemotherapy should be continued until it is no longer effective to be outrageous. I was encouraged by the naturopath to manage the project myself and to think of the doctors as subcontractors, who would help me deal with this crap. He encouraged me to make my own decisions and express my preferences before the medical staff. He told me that these decisions could prove fatal and that it was a matter for my life.

He said that he was an intelligent, learned man and that no one can match your level of responsibility and knowledge.

Charles Myers recently published an article that stated that patients who undergo chemotherapy live at least five years and not one year. This confirmed the information I had and reinforced my resolve to stop the chemotherapy.

— ◊ —

On Thursday, I was admitted for another treatment. This was my seventh treatment, and it was also the first in the third round. Before each treatment, I met with Dr. Bassam to discuss my case and to get his approval. After the fifteenth treatment, I made a decision to stop chemo.

I visited Dr. Bassam. His greatest asset was his willingness to listen to my wishes and not force me to do anything. He was open to all my requests regarding the treatment. The naturopath also suggested that I be the leader, and that he "only" was an advisor. Now, I was officially the project manager for my own survival. It was a little scary at first, but once it became clear that I was the project manager, it helped me to see the bigger picture and calm down, despite the immense responsibility.

I entered Dr. Bassam's office and walked into the treatment room. Ann was warm and welcoming as usual. It was a pleasure to see Ann, as she used to be called to me. It was much easier to get the IV because of our open relationship. Ann was an expert in pain therapy. This was crucial when treating cancer patients.

Ann asked me about interrupting the treatment, as it was described in the articles. I gave the article to Ann, which she found interesting. She called the nurse responsible and told her about the article. They were both thrilled. She assured me that Dr. Bassam would be open to my requests and opinions, and would work with me.

My regular chemo treatment began. We had been to Prague for a black theatre production the night before and returned home at three in morning. I felt quite tired so I took small doses every now and again throughout the treatment. Ann informed me at the end of treatment that my PSA level had dropped to 0.1 from 0.78. It was unbelievable to my ears. It was a wonderful response to the treatment. Before I left, we shook hands and made arrangements for my next treatment.

We drove that evening to my nephew Yoav's wedding at Sarona in a specially prepared field of wheat. It was amazing. The four columns of natural wood were used to build the wedding canopy. They were then fixed in the ground and the white fabric was stretched above them. It was also a beautiful ceremony. The Rabbi spoke about the relationship between the canopy structure, heaven and Earth, and Sharon, the bride, read something she wrote.

My illness made me a celebrity. Because of my cancer, people came to me more often than usual. Orna and her entire family were there when I met them. She was kind and supportive, and she invited us to visit her again. As a research assistant, she was involved in a study on genetic immunization of patients. This is the same topic that I wrote about in The Transformed Cell. I promised to send her the third copy of my manuscript.

I also met Dr. Ruthie. I was so glad to meet her, I lifted her up in the air and placed a few drops of water on her face. I shared with her what had happened and my faith in the medical system. She, too, agreed with me that I must take responsibility for my own life. The evening was pleasant and cool, which contributed to the relaxed atmosphere. Despite the fatigue and treatment that I had received in the morning, I felt fantastic.

— ◊ —

This heat was causing me to lose my balance. The dairy was the main problem. It was so humid and hot in the village that it really tortured me and my workers. A few fans were turned on and it helped a little. We couldn't resist installing air-conditioning because we knew it would make the workers and managers more comfortable as well as help us to make the cheese.

The price of Taxotere was reduced by 50 percent by the pharmaceutical company. Instead of paying $2,900 per monthly, I would pay only $1,450. Better than nothing.

Ruthie was the person I called to inquire about how she could obtain articles on Taxotere's benefits. Avivit once stated that if the drug was proven effective, the clinic would pay the balance. I approached the clinic to request funding for the treatment, but was turned down by the standard approach. I had planned to write to the clinic's CEO to ask for funding. But, I needed to find articles to support the treatment. Ruthie stated that the articles were provided by the drug retailer when we dealt with the funding for Zomera. I had previously asked the drug retailer for information, but she didn't respond. I called her back and she said that she would get it organized. Since I was in direct contact with him, I decided to approach her CEO directly if she didn't supply the articles.

Both healthy and sick people take medical tests to determine their physical condition. The blood count, for instance, tells doctors and us a lot about our body's strength, and function. The body's immunity level is determined by the number of white blood cells. Red blood cells show the ability of the body to transport oxygen to its body parts. CO_2 returns from the lungs are also indicated by red blood cells. Hemoglobin indicates the ability of the blood to carry oxygen. This establishes the range of results that is normal for healthy individuals. A deviation from the norm could indicate a disease or other abnormality in the body.

The patient and his medical team will have to decide how often they should perform these tests. It is crucial to assess the patient's current medical condition so that appropriate treatment can be given. However, it is important to consider other factors, such as whether or not the results of the tests will affect the patient's health. How fast is the expected increase in value? What is the cost of the test, and what are the psychological effects on the patient?

Two principles have greatly helped me in this fight as the manager of my project. The first principle was to know the current status of your illness at all times. This means that I need to perform PSA and other pertinent tests frequently so I can know my current condition at all times. The PSA test, a quick and inexpensive blood test, is available in 24 hours. To be able to give a clear assessment of my condition, I check my PSA at least once per month. When I was going through hormonal treatment, my PSA was falling. I noticed this in early 2002. That was when I realized that my treatment was at its best. From that point on, the PSA would begin to plateau before rising again. The nadir is the point at which any value, including the PSA, reaches its lowest point. At that point, my PSA was being checked every three weeks. Sometimes it was every two weeks. By knowing when my PSA was at its lowest point, I was able to recognize that treatment was over.

It is important to be ready for a change of treatment immediately.

This approach is not recommended by most oncologists. Oncologists usually advise prostate cancer patients that they monitor their PSA at least once every three months. This approach may be best for patients whose conditions are stable and there are no significant fluctuations. However, if fluctuations indicate that there is a change in severity of the illness, it is best that you are vigilant and regularly check the value to ensure that the information is current.

Second, I tried to keep the illness at its lowest possible level at all costs. This means that the PSA should not rise. This is obviously the ultimate goal for every patient fighting this disease. But there is another reason. Fighting this battle is easier when the PSA remains low. It is simple: A patient with a low

PSA and a remission of the disease will have fewer cancerous cells. This means that the patient's body and cancer are both weaker. This state is more favorable for treatment and will likely result in a longer-lasting cure. The PSA level is higher, which means that the disease spreads more widely, there are more cancerous cells, and the patient's ability to deal with it weakens. Any medical treatment that is not effective or lasts as long as it does will be less effective.

Bill Aishman explains this logic as follows:

It is better to fight cancer when the body and cancer are strong than when the cancer and body are weak.

My personal imagery world is directly connected to agriculture and the land. This situation is similar to a couch grass-covered vegetable patch. It spreads like a weed, and it's very difficult to eradicate. This is a problem that all farmers are aware of. It is much easier to remove this grass as it is still growing. It is almost impossible to eradicate once it has spread across an entire area if you don't get rid of it at the beginning.

Dr. Myers says that this principle is crucial in the fight against prostate cancer. One should do everything possible to keep the PSA low. Although this simple principle may seem obvious, there are many doctors who don't recognize its importance or do not follow it. In a few instances, I witnessed an oncologist trying to comfort a patient whose PSA was rising by saying "Let's see if it goes down a bit." It could be a temporary increase in PSA, or it isn't the end of the universe if it goes down a little." I am always disgusted by the oncologist who convinces patients to delay treatment for their advancing disease. This fails the patient in his fight against this horrible disease and reduces his ability manage it effectively.

Every month, I had blood tests. I was able to see the full extent of my condition through the results. They helped me to understand how to proceed with my treatments.

I had a great relationship with Dr. Nabil. Dr. Nabil was an advocate for testing. I didn't have to insist that I get tested at the frequency I chose.

This privilege is not available to all patients. I find out that their family doctor may not approve of them getting their PSA checked more frequently. They don't have any current information about their condition.

Nabil said that he had been recently examined by the regional head physician for a checkup. Nabil was complaining that he was referring patients too often to be tested and the doctor asked him to reduce his frequency. Dr. Nabil stated that Nabil refused to do this and that he could fire Nabil if he wanted. I was proud to be with my doctor, and felt fortunate to have him by my side.

— ◊ —

My constant concern with my disease made me a completely different person. Each person has a set or feelings, expectations, hopes, and sensations that guide his day. He has hopes for his family's future, his career, and he wants to see his children succeed in their lives. It is not even a thought that life expectancy can be considered.

My energy was focused on one goal as a cancer patient: survival. This meant that I had to take care of myself and find suitable treatments.

My uncertain future also affected any prospect or plan, as I immediately began to question whether it was relevant to my situation. This was evident when I was physically weaker. These thoughts took up less space when I was feeling normal. However, once I became a "project manager", I realized that I still had a few years to live. I felt calmer and more able to focus on my daily needs.

— ◊ —

Yesterday was the final round of chemotherapy. It was good to have two weeks to recover from the poison. I went to the clinic in the afternoon to get a prescription for Estracyt, one of my chemotherapy drugs. I would be taking it on the day of treatment and the next day. The pharmacy did not have the drug and neither did any other pharmacies. The second was that I had to pay $360 full price for it. I needed the drug the next day so I called the central pharmacy. They said the same thing: I had to order it in advance to get it. I was limited to trying to get it from the hospital doctors. This was the way I got it the first time. After several inquiries and refusing to take a dose that was expired for one year, I found the required dose with an expiration date of 2 months later. Great. I was saving money by getting a double dose. But I had to make sure that the drug was available for me later.

I appealed to the CEO of the clinic for Taxotere funding at $1,400 per month. I attached articles supporting the distribution of this drug to patients such as myself. These articles were provided by an Israeli drug distributor. I hoped that the CEO would agree. I was also burdened by this financial burden. It had heavily impacted the family's budget.

Ruthie called. Her husband and she had just returned from a trip in Greece. I asked her for her assistance in editing the last letter to the CEO. It was sent the next day, and I waited.

— ◊ —

Orr called from England where he was leading a camp for Jewish youth. He sounded much better than last week. We felt it was difficult for him to call us a week before. He seemed to be able to settle down. Rivka felt guilty for pushing him to this adventure. She seems to have gotten over it.

— ◊ —

It was hot again, and the dairy felt more like a warm bowl of soup. I was soaked in sweat when I returned home. Every year it was more difficult. The next day would be even more hot. The entire dairy area needed air conditioning. Yesterday I had to travel to Tel Aviv to do an errand at the dairy. This was not a wise decision, but I did take Bat-El along to assist me with any physical effort. I hoped that I wasn't doing any harm to myself. A nagging sensation was felt in my right groin, and right thigh. It would disappear in a few days, I prayed. Dr. Ruby advised me that it could be treated with radioactive therapy (I hoped it would not) by injecting strontium-89 into the vein.

It was something I kept in my mind in case I needed it.

— ◊ —

Yesterday was an amazing day. In the morning, I went to the clinic to get my Zoladex shot. Nurse Esther had given me the shot the first time and I asked her if it was possible to do it again. The substance is slowly dissolved over the three-month period by being injected under the skin on the stomach. She injected the substance deeper into my stomach, surprising me. I asked her about why she didn't inject it under my skin. She mumbled something about how wide the needle was and other nonsense.

Ruthie answered my question and explained that it is under the skin if you need slow absorption. "Which exactly is what this injection requires," I said to her. We agreed to consult Avivit about what to do.

After lunch, I drove to Tel Aviv in order to see the homeopathic doctor Orna, our relative had recommended. We then had to drive to the airport in order to receive Orr from England. Rivka and I met in Tel Aviv, and we drove together to the doctor for our four-o'clock appointment. We arrived slightly later than expected and settled in the waiting area. It was like a one-man show. He saw a lot of patients, each one paying anywhere from $150 to $300 for a fifteen-to-thirty-minute visit. The clinic exuded wealth, good taste and great taste. It was obvious that the doctor was very fond of money, and quite a lot. After thirty minutes, I approached the secretary to ask why we weren't admitted. After looking at her schedule, she realized that we had been written down for six rather than four. After leaving the clinic, we walked around Tel Aviv and then returned to the clinic a little later than six. We waited another half hour. The doctor was busy fixing his fax machine. He asked me about my condition when our meeting began. He explained that he was an excellent doctor who could treat cancer patients and had treated over fifteen thousand. He reached into his drawer and pulled out a sheet that he had prepared. It contained his instructions for the treatment. He then added my name to it and gave it to me.

In a few sentences, he explained to me the treatment he recommended. We got the impression that he was eager to see the next patient. He answered our questions very quickly. His phone rang shortly thereafter. His secretary called, asking him to finish. She stated that the queue in the waiting area was long. We ended up outside the secretary's office. We were charged $200 for a "first visit", she explained. She suggested that we buy the remedies at one of the pharmacies she provided, preferable the nearest one as the remedies were made on the spot. It is possible that they had a business relationship with the pharmacies. We purchased some of the products from a nearby pharmacy, and then paid an additional $300. This horrible disease is so expensive, my God!

It was already nine o'clock. Rivka was exhausted and I was hungry. We went to the Opera Tower's restaurant. I had sole fish and salad. We then went to a nearby Hotel. The hotel was small and dim, but it was comfortable enough to get a few hours sleep before we headed to the airport. I woke up at three in the morning and got into bed. After eating at the restaurant, I experienced terrible stomach cramps the next night. The alarm went off at 3:00 am. I was already suffering from food poisoning and went to the bathroom. There, I vomited my entire body. Rivka was thinking of driving me to the airport, but I managed to recover and I went to pick up the car. Rivka met me outside after gathering our belongings. It seemed like people were just getting out of the house, as though everyone was in full view.

After arriving at the airport at four in the morning, we waited to see our son. I looked for Rivka and then suddenly I heard someone behind me asking me if it was me looking for anyone. Orr was the one who called me. We hugged and kissed. We found Rivka and we hugged and kissed. We got in the car and drove back.

We decided to forgo seeing the homeopath. We were satisfied with just one visit.

— ◊ —

Rivka's parents visited us at midday. They did not ask me about my health, nor were they interested in the treatments I was receiving. Maybe it was the generation gap. In the case of my father, it was. As you get older, you become less interested in the problems of others and more focused on your own needs. Rivka's father could ramble on about the military 40 years ago and the financial state of the old-age club. I was bored to death by his endless stories and he failed to even ask about my condition.

— ◊ —

Yesterday was my weekly dose of poison chemo. I had to give blood prior to the treatment, and Dr. Bassam met me. I informed him that I would like to continue the treatment for six more months, and then I will stop. As usual, he was fair. Perhaps he was smarter than I thought. Maybe he didn't like to argue. However, I was still concerned. The discomfort I felt in my pelvis from the metastases was not going away even with chemotherapy. What if I stopped chemo?

Dr. Bassam was able to answer my questions about the injection that the nurse had given me into my abdominal cavity. I asked Dr. Bassam about the injection that was given to me into my abdomen cavity. He said that the rate at the which the substance dissolves was more important than its location, so there was no further action. Ruthie sought Avivit's advice on the matter. She gave me an odd answer: apparently, the manufacturer had altered the instructions for injecting the substance into the abdomen. That was what I had to confirm.

Dr. Ruby suggested that two additional cancer markers be tested. Dr. Bassam was as prudent about testing and asked me why. In some cases, the PSA didn't move in certain cases. However, there was a possibility that the cancer was changing. Therefore, it seemed prudent to test these additional markers before and after chemotherapy. He was happy to agree and directed the doctor to conduct these tests.

Despite my fears and uncertainty, I returned home feeling happy and fulfilled after the treatment. The PSA was 0.04 This was a remarkable decline, which showed that the cancer had been suppressed to an undetectable PSA level. It could not be detected. This gave me hope that I was on a good path (until further notice).

That morning, a friend asked me how I was doing. I replied that I was fine for the moment. I told her that I was quite well for now.

I received some information from patients' forums about strontium-89. Dr. Ruby suggested it as a way of suppressing metastases. One person argued that the treatment caused damage to the bone marrow, immune system, and made one more susceptible to infection. It didn't sound fun.

— ◊ —

Ruthie called the morning to inquire if Avivit called me to obtain information about the letter addressed to the CEO concerning Taxotere funding. She hadn't. I promised to call her that night, but she said that she wouldn't be home the next two nights. It seemed like the treatment was delayed. I would need to spend $1,500 more for the next round. I was mad again. I spent more and more money. But what about the people who don't have any? They just die.

— ◊ —

I had to have more chemotherapy on Thursday. Ten treatments were left. I was mixed about the next step. I had mixed feelings about the next step. On one hand I wanted those terrible treatments to end, and on the other I was anxious about the day they would end. What will happen to my condition? Is my disease likely to spread?

Before the treatment began, Dr. Bassam asked me when I wanted the chemotherapy to end. He explained that he was hearing more and more about the technique of interrupting chemotherapy. After having told me months ago that I should continue with the chemotherapy as long as it was working, he asked me again. He said that he had had a patient who had received chemotherapy for over a year. Did he know that I was the one who first introduced him to this method?

Taxotere was the main chemotherapy drug. I've mentioned it a few times. It was partially subsidized by the government, but I had to pay full price because it wasn't prescribed for prostate cancer. Breast and lung cancer patients were able to receive funding from the Ministry of Health, while prostate cancer patients (like myself) had to pay full price. Patients sitting in the treatment room next to me were receiving the same drug, fully funded by Ministry of Health. It was a luxury that I could afford. What would a patient who is less financially stable than me do? You would be forced to give up the treatment. It was only a theoretical question at the time. But what if other patients were to follow suit and require this treatment in the future?

The treatment room on the oncological ward was run by Nurse Mimi. Three months had passed since I first heard from Nurse Mimi that I was out-of-pocket for the drug. She pulled me aside when I arrived for my final round and asked if I was purchasing Taxotere privately. I replied, "Yes," she said. What other options do I have?

She was reprimanded. "Why didn't you say anything?" It would have been easy for me to give it to

You are welcome to use it for no cost. You might find the exact dose that you require here. I asked her.

She smiled in secret.

I refused to give up, and she said that sometimes she would get a supply for patients who needed only a small amount. Sometimes, a patient would stop receiving treatment or die and she would keep any leftovers.

She instructed me to "Don't Buy Any More".
Her gesture touched me deeply and I thanked her for it with tears in my eyes. It was a great relief not to have to pay for Taxotere and work towards funding it.

— ◊ —

I sent an email to my "Australian friend". I had lost contact with him for some time. I asked him about his treatment plans and he replied in full detail. He was on a different path. He had completed six months of chemotherapy and his PSA was less than 0.05. After that, he decided to stop taking hormonal treatments. Instead, he began taking another set, one that regulates testosterone, and another that boosts immunity. He was taking between thirty and forty pills per day. I wrote back to him asking for clarification about his treatment. I was pondering whether I could use his consultation services. He was able to get his consultation online so why shouldn't I? There were two downsides to this. The first was that I wouldn't be able to get all the drugs he suggested in Israel. And the second was the financial aspect of my consultation as well as the price of medication. It was worth my time to look into it.

Leah, our American friend, was staying with us over the weekend. Her mother was suffering from terminal, severe cancer and was near the end of her days. Her lungs were filled with water and she was admitted to the hospital. Although the doctors wanted to drain her fluid, she was unable to coagulate properly and they tried to stabilize her condition. It reminded me of my mother's last stages of her illness. Ironically, Leah's mother rejected and marginalized her throughout her entire life. Yet, she continued to care for her mother with utmost devotion.

— ◊ —

Two reasons were the reason I hadn't written in a month. First, I was busy communicating with Dr. Tuck (the doctor who treated my friend from Australia). I asked him to consult me. After I told them about it on Rosh Hashanah, Zvika, an eye doctor and my brother Arieh, encouraged me to ask him.

My soul also needed some time off from intensive writing.

This is great news. Nurse Ann informed me with excitement that my PSA reading was 0. The previous test result was 0.04. I couldn't contain my excitement. I hugged her, and placed a wet kiss on her cheek. It couldn't get better or more perfect.

It was time to ask: What next?

To my best knowledge, I was presented with two options:

The first was to stop the chemotherapy but continue with the hormonal treatment. Zoladex injections were given once every three months along with another treatment using a few cancer suppressant drugs.

There are many cancer suppressants available, some of them available in Israel, and others that are not. Proscar, calcitriol (the active component in vitamin D), and thalidomide are just a few of the many cancer suppressants on this list. These prevent new blood vessels from developing which is necessary for the growth of cancer cells.

The main problem with this method, according to me, was the continual hormonal treatment. This caused testosterone levels to fall, thereby causing severe damage to the body. The Israeli medical establishment accepted this option more or less.

The second option was the one I hoped Dr. Tuck would suggest to me. This would stop Zoladex from being administered and allow testosterone to return to its natural levels.

The best way to increase testosterone is to attach patches to your body. This allows testosterone to penetrate the skin. This approach has the advantage of restoring the patient to a normal testosterone level. The cancer will develop slowly from that point and can be maintained for a long period of time with the help cancer suppressants. If cancer erupted again, you resumed hormonal treatment. The body returns to almost normal function, at least for a short time.

If he felt me ready, I thought about going for it.

To send Dr. Tuck my medical record, I translated it all into English and edited it so that it could be transferred electronically. Dr. Ruthie was a great help in translating and editing the material. I didn't hear back from Dr. Ruthie for a week. I was also asked for my biopsy slides, and I was waiting for them to be sent to the lab.

Since I was nearing the end of my fifth round of chemotherapy with a positive PSA reading, I was anxious to find out what the doctor had in store for me.

Apart from that, I also experienced severe stomach pain. The first occurred in my middle-upper stomach. I was in pain and started to writhe. I finally gave up and called Rivka. I was examined by the doctors and given a painkiller. The pain disappeared almost immediately, and I believe it was even before the medication was administered. I was greeted by a young and friendly doctor. She had sour semen-like odor. It was likely that she was on a rush and didn't have the time to shower before going to work. It was Wednesday night just before I had my weekly treatment. The next morning, I was discharged from the emergency department and immediately went to the oncology unit to receive my chemotherapy.

After I had finished working in the garden with Orr, the second attack in my right upper stomach occurred. Perhaps I exerted too much effort. The pain subsided within a few hours. I didn't know the cause of my recurring stomach pains.

Also, I felt burning sensations in my bladder when I peed. It was a horrible torture. Dr. Ruby diagnosed it as a urinary tract infection. It was likely that my weak immune system from chemotherapy caused it. He advised me to seek antibiotic treatment from my family physician. I called Dr. Nabil and he prescribed antibiotic medication. He left the prescription at the pharmacy on Friday afternoon and we took it with us to Sarona. It was much easier to manage this complicated project with the help of doctors. That was a good thing.

My mother was buried in Sarona. Here is a portion of my journal that I wrote about the difficult part of saying goodbye to a dying person. It was also interesting to see that Dina felt the same way, even though she seemed to have said goodbye. It is important to note that she was not able to talk about her feelings about her approaching death, in a way that would have allowed her to accept it. Lawrence LeShan's Cancer as a Turning Point suggests that this might be because no one had spoken directly with her.

— ◊ —

I looked at the table that I had created about my achievements, aspirations, and what I would never achieve in my lifetime. It made me feel more positive than I did when I first wrote it. I felt encouraged. Despite my zero PSA level, it added to my optimism. However, it was obvious that the battle was only just beginning.

TAXOTERE'S IDEAL EFFECTS

Many side effects are associated with chemotherapy drugs. These medications, which can be very aggressive, can cause severe side effects. Taxotere can cause two major side effects over time. The first is the potential to develop infections under the nails. The second is numbness. These side effects include nausea, loss in taste and other secondary side effects.

Taxotere, a relatively new drug, has so far not been associated with any side effects. It was not known at the time that Taxotere could cause under-nail infection. Long-term use may cause actual nail loss. Bill Aishman's nails did indeed fall off over time and he had to use bandages at his tips to keep them from falling off.

The side effect of an under-nail infection had already been known when I started the chemotherapy protocol. Nurse Ann suggested that I dip my fingers into ice water. I didn't understand the connection between ice water and chemotherapy. I was told by her that ice water cools the fingers and decreases blood flow. This reduces the amount of chemotherapy reaching the fingertips, which helps to prevent infections under the nails. There was no risk to me, as cancer doesn't spread beyond the fingertips. I was also offered an "ice cap", which would prevent hair loss, based on the same logic. I said no. It can also freeze my brain. To keep my hair from falling out, there was a limit. Nurse Ann gave me a bowl filled with water and ice cubes. This was a lot of fun. It was freezing cold. It was obvious that I should remove my fingers from the water, but my nails had to be protected. I came up with a compromise. I reached for the air and pulled my fingers out of the pain. I was careful not to do too much, so I put my fingers back in and continued the process. After each treatment was over, I breathed a sigh of relief and buried my hands in my pockets to heat them up.

It was very helpful to use the ice bath. The treatment did not cause any problems with my fingernails. A year after the treatment, I noticed something under my big toenail. It started to swell up and redden. It was a mystery to me. I reached into the pain right at its center. Yellow puss began to ooze from the tiny hole in my nail. It slowly healed after I sterilized it. Is Taxotere still effective? It was difficult to believe. However, it was something I'd never experienced before.

The most annoying side effect of Taxotere (peripheral Neuropathy) is numbness. Taxotere can cause numbness in the legs for patients who have taken large amounts. The numbness can spread to the whole body if it is not stopped. It's like having hundreds of ants crawling all over you, bugging you relentlessly. This can make a person insane. This phenomenon is not limited to the night. It can disrupt a patient's sleep, causing them to lose their quality of life.

Numbness can be a result of peripheral neural diseases such as diabetes, thyroid problems or overdrinking. It is also associated with prolonged chemotherapy exposure. This unpleasant condition can also be caused by long-term exposure to drugs that lower blood lipids or cholesterol.

This phenomenon was something I knew about, and I was concerned that it would pay me a visit if I continued with treatment for too long. This was yet another reason to end treatment right away and not wait until it stops working, as Dr. Bassam suggested.

Mine caused nausea, sometimes vomiting, as with all chemo protocols. The antinausea drug prevents the vomiting reflex. It's a small, pink pill that I was given during treatment. Although I didn't feel nauseated, I felt constipated shortly afterwards. Ann asked me, "Is it related?" Ann answered, "Yes," I asked. The pill causes constipation but prevents nausea. It was like having to choose between cholera and typhoid. Constipation is not a plague mentioned in the Holy Bible. My stomach was swelling up and there was no way to release it. To relieve the pressure, I had to resort to one of the horrible remedies.

Ann agreed to only give me half of the pill and I chose to go with the nausea. I found that I didn't feel nausea even with the lower dose. I decided to ask Ann not to give me the deceitful pill in the next treatment. The pink pill was removed and I waited for the nausea to pass. It was a disappointment. I felt very little nausea. I stopped taking antinausea drugs during treatment, and didn't feel any nausea.

---

9 The Jewish New Years.

CHAPTER NINE

CONSULTING AN AMERICAN ONCOLOGIST

October 2002 to Early January 2003

Following Dr. Tuck's recommendations regarding my next stage of treatment, I did so. It felt like a new chapter had opened in my life. The moment I started to read the recommendations, it was clear that he was talking business. He was very thorough in his analysis and explanation of my medical condition. This was evident in the email I sent to him. It earned me my trust. He noted that his recommendations were based on material he had received from me, likely to avoid any potential lawsuits.

Dr. Tuck advised me to stop chemotherapy at that point and switch to Nizoral, also known as ketoconazole, as well as hydrocortisone. These drugs were used as a second line of hormonal treatment to treat prostate cancer patients. He advised me to continue with this treatment until mid November, when the Zoladex injection would stop working. This happens in twelve weeks. He said that he would recommend that the next step be taken towards November.

Dr. Tuck recommended Ketoconazole to stop the adrenal gland's hormonal production. The gland also produces dihydrotestosterone which is another hormone that can accelerate the growth of prostate cancer. The adrenal gland produces dihydrotestosterone and other steroids necessary for proper bodily function. Hydrocortisone pills are required to compensate for the loss of steroids caused by ketoconazole. The exact dosage must be determined based on the patient's needs. Hydrocortisone deficiency can cause severe physical and even death. Hydrocortisone-treated patients must inform their doctors if they lose consciousness.

Alternately Dr. Tuck recommended a low-dose combination of preventive drugs that included thalidomide and Leukine. These drugs are intended to increase a patient's immune systems. He also suggested that I artificially increase my testosterone by placing testosterone patches on my body. It sounded intriguing and was exactly what my Australian friend recommended.

This treatment presented two problems for me: It was expensive and I was unsure if I could afford it. Second, it wasn't effective, even though it was recommended to many patients.

This technique to raise the testosterone levels in prostate cancer patients is completely different from the usual treatments. It's almost like trying to light a bonfire with a gallon fuel. This method is rejected by the American medical establishment. This is why Dr. Tuck, and Dr. Leib, his partner, are continually and publicly criticised.

Despite my fears, I accepted his advice and stopped the chemotherapy. This meant that on Thursday, two days later, I would "happy" receive my final chemo dose. I hoped that the next phase would not come at all, or be much further down the road.

— ◊ —

Izhar, my brother, was there with me for my last chemotherapy. He brought his video camera. It was a great day. I picked him up at the train station that morning. A security guard stopped us at the hospital's entrance and asked for permission to bring a camera inside. We asked the security guard for his permission. He stated that he would need to obtain approval from the hospital's chief nurse. We told him that we had the approval from the ward. But that didn't help. With an air of authority, he called the head nurse to inform us that he had contacted the hospital director. I asked him to speak with the head nurse at the ward. Finally, he accepted and spoke with the head nurse on the ward. She immediately confirmed the matter. After waiting for about 20 minutes at the gate, we were finally granted permission to enter the hospital with the camera. Izhar seized the opportunity to film the security guard "doing his work" with the hidden camera.

We went to Dr. Bassam. Izhar had already told me that he wanted to see Dr. Bassam.

To film the meeting, I needed permission from Dr. Bassam. Although it was uncomfortable, I agreed to film the meeting. I found this doctor to be a very pleasant man. He was willing to accommodate almost all my requests, even the request for the meeting to be recorded. He was always raving about the cheese that I brought to him from the dairy. He seemed more interested in the cheese than he was about me. He was open to discussing the issues of marketing cheese with me. I was sure that I would offer him a job at my dairy. During the meeting I stated that I felt great and that I was going to follow Dr. Tuck's advice to stop the chemotherapy today. I gave him a complete copy of the doctor's recommendations.

He said he would read them, and we agreed that we would talk about them at the next meeting. I hoped that he would actually read them. As Dr. Tuck requested, I asked him to examine my lung CT to determine if there were any absorptions or swelling. Dr. Bassam looked at my images randomly and concluded that there was nothing. He even included it in my medical file to prove that he meant it. It was something I wasn't convinced of. I was suspicious of these experts and found myself questioning their claims many times. Although I admit that I may be exaggerating, I believe I am right. Sometimes they were correct, but sometimes, at crucial crossroads they did not know. In my case, as with many others, it was a matter if life or death. Avivit even showed us two spots in the X-ray, and the radiologist who decoded the test said that there were two absorptions.

Izhar, upon leaving the office, told me that he was shocked at Dr. Bassam's negligence. "Why aren't you surprised?" "I answered." After every meeting with him, I have been keeping a journal about it."

We found our way to the treatment area. Izhar placed his camera beside me. Nurse Ann futzed about me, prepping the IV and allowing the drugs to flow into my body. I had come to accept the reality of chemotherapy as a routine. Izhar expressed an interest in Dr. Tuck's recommendations and I began to read the letter I held in my hand and explain it. Gradually I felt like I was getting lost in detail while Izhar didn't have the right background. It felt like I was becoming my father. He would often go into great detail about a topic and then realize it was time for me to stop.

Izhar shared with me his story of how he had an idea to make a movie while on a train ride. My idea was for a narrator to read from my journal and then show relevant shots. He liked the idea but it was important to create a plan for the film. We had to first decide the film's purpose. I shared with him an example of my engineering work. It is important to create technical specifications for every project. These specifications should include performance data. The same approach should be applied to a film. Although engineering performance is not necessary, it is important that you are focused and know who your target audience is. Perhaps it is to send a message about the importance and importance of early detection and treatment of cancer. If so, the film should be shown before the appropriate audience. He didn't say it directly, but I believe I convinced him.

After the treatment, Izhar drove to Nahariya where he sat down in a cafe. Izhar pulled out his notebook and asked me some interesting questions. He had read in my journal about the "sorceress", and how the horse fell asleep on the horse's shoulder. Could he interview her? He also wanted to interview Dr. Solan. I assured him that it would not be a problem to interview the "sorceress", but I didn't know much about Dr. Solan. He agreed to ask me. I thought, "My younger brother has a lot more guts." Kudos to him. Izhar was then taken to the train station. I enjoyed spending the day with him and felt the need to let him know. As we parted ways, I told him how much I enjoyed our time together.

— ◊ —

As I said, Dr. Tuck recommended that I stop the chemotherapy. Although I thought that bureaucratic matters would be easier now that Taxotere was out of my control, I discovered that I had to go through the same process for all three drugs Dr. Tuck recommended, even though they were funded by Ministry of Health. This was also something. Mickey, Nahariya's pharmacy owner, was a friend and colleague. He also happens to be the head the Israeli pharmacists' association. This could prove useful when bureaucracy becomes too rigid, as I soon discovered.

After I had obtained all three prescriptions, the pharmacy gave me two of them. They didn't have hydrocortisone on hand. I tried to find the place I could buy it, but there was a problem with claiming it because of a bureaucratic glitch. I felt that I had to have the hydrocortisone regardless of what. The use of Nizoral can cause a deficiency in hydrocortisone, which can be dangerous. You cannot have one without the other.

I ran to Dr. Ruthie. She suggested that I see Dr. Tuck. I also emailed Dr. Tuck that night to inquire about prednisone. I used the chance to ask him when he would start the medication, as it may be wise to have a break in between chemotherapy and the new treatment. The same night, I received a clear and decisive answer about when the new treatment would begin. It was summarized in one word: NOW. He was much more cautious about the prednisone. He sent me the dose via email, but stated that he would need to double-check it later. Ruthie and me decided to try again for the hydrocortisone. Soon after, she joyfully announced that the drug was in stock at a nearby pharmacy and promised to keep it for her.

We agreed that I would fax the prescription to her so she could pick it up at the pharmacy. We had planned to travel to Jerusalem on Friday so I thought we could stop by her house and pick it up. I called the pharmacy to find out how much they had. It turned out they had already sold the drug to another person. It was unbelievable! I called Mickey quickly and he said he would try to help. He called all of the top echelons of Israel's pharmaceutical industry, including the Chief Pharmacist at the Ministry of Health. They told him the problem. The ministry required the drug manufacturer to renew its production line. Due to its short shelf-life, the first batch of this new production line was disqualified. Over the telephone, the chief pharmacist told Mickey that the batch disqualified was garbage. Mickey spoke with her and said that she would personally provide me the quantity I required if it was not available elsewhere. Mickey said that the drug was safe to use, but it had a shorter expiration.

Mickey created a new channel of communication by mass emailing all pharmacies asking for hydrocortisone. He called me in the afternoon to inform me that the pharmacy near Haifa had the drug on hand, but it would only last ten days. They promised to hold the medication. I called them to ask. I promised to drive there the next day to pick it up. Ruthie was the one I called and she told me all. She was sorry for not being there.

I replied, "What does it mean that you couldn't help me?" You're my rock, you help me every day. That was how I felt. Without her, what would I do?

She replied, "I am more like a broken Reed." She suggested that I take the first Nizoral tablet the same night as I was receiving the hydrocortisone next day. I followed her lead, and soon after I noticed my vision blurring slightly, I started to feel it. This was a side effect of the drug, I thought. I was worried about the effects on my driving, as I was required to take it three times daily. I could not drive if I took it three times a day. As I understood it, sticky feet and palms could also be side effects. I was told by the guys on the forum that sticky palms and feet could be caused by placing a hand like this on a piece of paper. (Very funny). It made me wonder what would happen if you went barefoot around your house. This could be an alternative option to vacuuming. This is in addition to the nausea, diarrhea and other diseases I was hoping not to encounter.

— ◊ —

I went to the pharmacy on Friday morning to pick up my hydrocortisone tablets. I also requested Zomera which I was supposed receive at the hospital on Thursday. However, the pharmacist said that they had not received the prescription. Dr. Nabil assured me that he would fax it to them. He was always so dedicated and responsible! She said it couldn't be. But she tried again, and it was not there. I called Dr. Nabil who said he had twice faxed my prescription! I called Dr. Nabil to verify the correct fax number. The pharmacist searched again, but this time she found the prescription. She then informed me that she still needed my original prescription. I was puzzled as to why this had happened. I had been sending them the same prescription every six months. Why was she suddenly requiring the original? I promised to send it to her thinking that she would give the drug. She said that she had lost the funding approval to get the drug through the health clinic and she couldn't give it to me. I would need to provide a new confirmation to get the drug. I thought I was going to explode. I couldn't contain my anger and said that I needed to get approval within the week. It takes two weeks at most. Another pharmacist at a nearby counter suggested that I could pass by the pharmacy and get approval when you went in for my treatment.

"But I don't live here!" I replied.

She replied from a far corner of the pharmacy with at least ten customers listening in.

"But, you're treated in the hospital at Haifa."

This was the final straw. "Don't interfere with my treatments," I shouted.

I explained to the pharmacist that it was a problem with payment and that she could resolve it.

She concluded, "You won't get it." Loud and clear: "I'm going to keep my license.".

What else can I say? I am a proud victim of bureaucracy. I tried to reach the pharmacy manager who I had met during my unusual drug use, but she refused to talk to me. I was confused. I called the person in charge. It turned out that it was the same pharmacist who worked at the faraway counter. I wanted to talk to her discreetly.

"Look," I replied. "Look," I said.

As I stood there, I felt the tears welling up in my eyes. I quickly put my dark sunglasses over my prescription glasses. Oversensitivity was a common symptom of the disease. I couldn't control it when it grabbed me.

She said that she knew, but was certain that the drug would be paid for if it wasn't approved.

She suggested that we swipe my credit card to guarantee it. I agreed and was soon outside, with Zomera and hydrocortisone for Thursday. It felt great! Although I had only a 10-day supply, I was ready for the short-term. I ran home. We went to Jerusalem for a weekend to see Izhar, Irit.

— ◊ —

Five days had passed since the last treatment. Side effects were not too severe. One side effect was the possibility of being blinded from the sun. To help with this problem, I bought sunglasses that could be clipped over my prescription glasses. But I had to remember to take them with me everywhere. A second phenomenon I noticed, and which my brothers had taught me, was the feeling of sticky fingers in my hands and around my neck. It felt like I had rubbed resin into those areas. It brought me back to my childhood. I was able to recall the tiny pine grove that existed between my grandparents' house and our hut, where resin would stick to my hands. Other than that, there were no other side effects.

This treatment was more difficult because I had to be very disciplined about taking the pills. To maintain an acidic environment in my stomach and mouth, I took two hydrocortisone tablets with breakfast. Two hours later, I took a Nizoral tablet on an empty stomach with a glass of Coke. Two hours later, I took more Nizoral with the same acidic method. Then, two hours later, I took another Nizoral with food. A Proscar tablet before bedtime. Not to mention the vitamins and other supplements. Look at all the pills I was taking. It's no wonder that I felt like a walking pillbox.

Daily Pill Consumption

Time	Pill	Quantity	Directions
	Hydrocortisone	2	With food
Morning	Vitamin D	1	With food
	Calcium	1	With food
Two hours after breakfast	Nizoral	1	With Coke
Two hours after lunch	Nizoral	1	With Coke

	Hydrocortisone	1	With food
	Calcium	2	With food
Dinner	Selenium	1	With food
	Vitamin E	1	With food
	Vitamin D	2	With food
	Lycopene	1	With food
Two hours after dinner	Nizoral	1	With Coke
At bedtime	Proscar	1	

It was difficult to get out of my house carrying all the pills. This was in addition to the strict diet I was following. My friends and colleagues suggested that I go to Israel or travel abroad. This was awkward, and nobody understood it. It was a feeling I experienced over the weekend at Izhar. To make sure that I took my pills on time, I kept my eyes on the Coke bottle and the pillbox.

— ◊ —

The speakers were connected to my computer. Now, I could write while listening to the radio. Music lifted my spirits. The singer of the year was playing a loop in the living room. On his last trip to Tel Aviv, Orr purchased his CD. Amir also liked him. He was so much fun to watch that I couldn't wait for him to stop being such a great friend.

We spent last weekend in Jerusalem, as I mentioned, with Izhar (and Irit). As part of his healing support for me, Izhar took me on a ride on his bike towards the end of the evening. Irit and Ovadi, my cousin, drove behind us in the car and she filmed. It is a lot of fun to ride a motorcycle. You can feel the distance covered and the wind blowing in you face, unlike a car. It leaves all cars behind, especially when it turns green, is what makes me adrenaline pump. Their constant efforts to help me moved me equally. I felt that they used to think, "Yes, let's give him a good time with what little he has left." I felt more confident about my future and was able to joyfully accept all the attention I received.

Izhar asked me during the ride if I wanted the film edited like a documentary and shown to a wider audience than my family. This type of film is more challenging, but I found it to be more enjoyable. It remains to be seen.

— ◊ —

Yesterday I went to the hospital for my Zomera treatment. Before the treatment, I met Dr. Bassam. He told me that he had read Dr. Tuck's recommendations and was impressed with them. He also agreed to stop the chemotherapy. He also asked me about my relationship with Dr. Tuck and for his website address. It took only an hour and a quarter to complete the treatment, which was a tremendous relief. After the treatment, I went to Nahariya pharmacy to replenish my hydrocortisone. I was able to get another packet at the Haifa pharmacy that would last me for ten more days. I went to pick it up, before it vanished. I quickly grabbed lunch at Nahariya's regular hummus place and raced to Haifa. After getting the pills from the pharmacy I realized it was time for me to take the Nizoral tablet two hours later than I had eaten. I ran back home quickly because it was not my turn. I arrived at the pharmacy around three in the afternoon. I gulped my pills with a Coke, and then went to sleep. I was ready to leave for another meeting about Teva Ez at five. I felt tired and fatigued during the meeting, possibly because of the Zomera treatment. The treatment was also responsible for the pain in my right pelvic bone.

— ◊ —

It was a week. My last PSA reading read 0.04. It's pretty good considering my previous PSA reading was zero. It was difficult to tell if the increase was due to the measurement tool or an actual deviation. Last Tuesday, I did another PSA measurement to make sure there wasn't an uphill trend. Tomorrow would be my results. I was curious about where this was leading. After taking a three-week break from chemo, and two weeks after starting the Nizoral/hydrocortisone, there were moments when I felt like this treatment wasn't going well. While I felt like I was getting energy back, my pelvis discomfort returned. It was both confusing and frustrating. I hope that this will not lead to me returning to chemo. Ruthie and I discussed it yesterday. We agreed to wait for tomorrow's PSA results, perform another bone scan, then consult Dr. Tuck once again.

Mickey, Nahariya's pharmacist, ordered another packet of hydrocortisone from Haifa. This resource was available to me, so I had enough for three more weeks until mid November. Who would have thought? Maybe I wouldn't need more. As a gesture of gratitude, I sent Mickey a cheese delivery.

We went on Sunday to a beautiful family outing with Arieh, Dina and my father, to a restaurant further north. Dina had been hinting at her desire to meet for some time. It was also something I needed. Instead of taking them to Mitzpe Hila for dinner, I suggested that we meet halfway. It would be a nice change from our usual dinner at home. Arieh had a draft of the contract that he and his potential partner brought to me so I could offer my opinions. Dina and Arieh heard about my new treatment and the American doctor's suggestions. Dina was fascinated by these stories of my flirtation with death, which I shared with my closest friends. It was something I felt the need for, and it gave me a sense of catharsis. Maybe it was my spiritual need that allowed me to live on the edge for extended periods of time and keep my sanity. We kept each other updated on "agricultural" issues in every meeting. Arieh shared with me details about the fence he built in his barn to protect against thieves. I also received news from the dairy regarding the cheese, etc.

It was a joy to see our family relationships growing stronger. It was clear that my disease was the direct cause of this. Another positive thing about my scum.

Today, I went for a walk around Nahariya. It was beautiful. People were sitting in cafes laughing and focusing on their daily business. I wondered if these people knew how fortunate they were, how happy they should feel, and how much this world could do for someone like me in the middle of their lives. Although it may not have been noticed, I felt like I had a verdict hanging over me, almost as though I was being executed. It kept me awake and busy from the time I woke up until the time I went to bed, sometimes even into the night. It was as if I was running in the wrong direction on a conveyor belt that led into a dark abyss. I tried my best to not be taken by it. It was impossible for me to get off of it, so I knew that it would eventually lead me there.

When I felt good, I could live my life like anyone else.

For a while, I was contemplating an idea. The existing treatments did not result in recovery. It was a temporary lull. I considered upgrading existing techniques to better serve my patient.

Galil Medical is a subsidiary of the engineering company I left before getting sick. It uses night vision cameras that I used to work for my old employers. The detector must be kept at a very low temperature in order to allow it to work. It should be around minus 200degC. This technology allows the company to cool down a small set of needles that are used to treat prostate carcinoma. The tiny ice balls created by the freezing of the needles in the prostate can be used to destroy the cancerous tissue. This works in cases where the cancer has not spread.

I thought it would be a good idea to expand the use this technology to kill bone metastases and bring about a significant remission. These metastases can also cause pain. The only metastases that could be treated with radiation were those that posed a threat to patient's life. Radiation has the disadvantage that it can also burn healthy tissue near the metastases, causing damage to existing nerves and other side effects.

Over a week had passed since I tried to contact Galil Medical's main developer. Reuven was his name and he seemed like a nice man. He was due to meet me the next Wednesday. Although I knew that he was unlikely to make my idea a reality, it was worth the effort. If it came down to it, I would be willing to be the Guinea Pig if it was worth it.

— ◊ —

I felt awful again. It was apparent that the American doctor's treatment wasn't working and I felt like my physical condition was getting worse. It was very painful to feel the metastasis in my right pelvis. I felt tingling and needling sensations in my prostate. I considered this another sign of a bad diagnosis. Two days prior, I had written Dr. Tuck asking for his advice. I didn't receive a response for a day so I emailed his secretary asking her to remind him. She also informed me that if there were any financial issues, they should charge credit to my card. The next day, Dr. Tuck emailed me and advised me to continue with my treatment. He also apologized for the delay. I wrote him again tonight, stating that my condition was not satisfactory and that I needed to make changes. I was hopeful that he would quickly respond with positive ideas. Since I stopped chemo, I felt that my condition had worsened. It is physically impossible to continue chemo for an indefinite period of time. My deterioration has been so rapid, it is both scary and amazing. Two weeks ago I felt so energized and happy, but now everything is crumbling like a stack of cards.

— ◊ —

The next day I met Dr. Reuven of Galil Medical to discuss the treatment of metastases. We were both engineers so we quickly became friends. Right from the beginning, I showed him a picture of my bone scan. His shocked expression was unintentional as he saw the sizes of the metastases (or absorptions) in the photo. He tried to keep his face straight, but I was able to see his surprise. It was an interesting meeting, and he didn't disqualify me. He stated that technology was readily available and not restricted. Medical limitations were the limitation. It was necessary to find a medical radiologist capable of performing interventional radiology. This would be enough to support the Helsinki Committee's approval. The Helsinki Committee approves human trials based on the Helsinki regulations. Galil Medical had the technology for freezing bone tumors, but it was specifically designed to treat bone cancer. Doctors can expose bone cancer tumors during surgery and freeze them. He promised me his cooperation with such doctors and even promised to make a needle of custom-size in the event that such a trial took place. We needed to find a prominent clinical radioologist who could and would promote this. This technique will not reduce the number of cancer cells in your body and it won't lead to recovery. It was unclear to me whether there was any benefit to this.

— ◊ —

In the meantime, Dr. Tuck replied to me. I noticed a little impatience from him. He suggested that I increase my hydrocortisone intake. Maybe that's why I wasn't feeling well. I hoped that he was right. Although I had increased my dose from the previous day, I felt that something was still wrong in my body. However, the sensations were less severe than before. Today, I had to take another PSA test at my clinic. It would reveal the direction of my disease. It was a very anxious moment for me.

My Zomera was extended for six more months thanks to funding from the clinic. I also discovered that hydrocortisone is available at the clinic's pharmacy. Nahariya was promised that they would send it. Although I wasn't clear as to why the drug suddenly became available, they gave me a detailed explanation about why it wouldn't be available for the next few months. Was my request a catalyst for the drug being made available to me? This pathetic disease is not easy to manage.

— ◊ —

Dr. Tuck was contacted by me to let him know that something wasn't working for me and that I felt unwell. Dr. Tuck replied that it sounded odd to him and that he didn't know how to help me further. Everything seems to be falling apart. Rivka said that the American doctor who was almost a God to me didn't know what to do about me.

Yesterday, I spoke with Dr. Ruby to discuss my relationship with the U.S. Clinic and my distress. To clarify my situation, he suggested that I take some more tests. I sent Dr. Tuck the information I had. Dr. Ruby is both a true professional and a mansch. He is a patient-oriented doctor who speaks with patience and reason. He can also analyze medical situations with great logic. He has a lot of common sense in handling the outrageous battle that I am leading.

— ◊ —

Today I went to the clinic to get my PSA results. It was a huge zero. It was very nice. We hope it stays like that. Maybe all this chaos was just me.

Later, I drove with Lenny and Leny to Tel Aviv to meet the CEO of Israel Cancer Association. We wanted to create an association that would represent the interests of patients with prostate cancer. In an effort to represent patients' rights, it would be run under the auspices Israel Cancer Association. It went well. It was discovered that the Israel Cancer Association had an umbrella organization for all health-related organizations. It was named Zvi (Israel Health Consumers), and Meidad Gissin was its head. He knew everything about the medical establishment and who was who. To help develop the idea for a new organization, he would be attending the Haifa support group meeting. We discussed the fact that the public was not paying attention to prostate cancer and patients were not receiving the care they need. I explained to the CEO that although there was plenty of information on breast cancer, the bulletin board at her office did not have any information about prostate cancer. We also discussed drugs that had been approved for breast cancer patients (e.g Taxotere) but not for prostate cancer patients.

I felt good after this trip. I felt better. Maybe it was the increased energy I felt from the meeting, or perhaps it was the combination of the PSA results and a break in the routine that caused it. Dr. Tuck needed to know about my progress. We were to make a decision on the next stage of treatment by the middle of the month. This was my next challenge. I stopped writing the next day.

I wrote Dr. Tuck to report the changes in my condition. He also offered additional suggestions. We will soon decide whether I want to stop taking Ketoconazole as he suggested and to switch to maintenance treatments to prevent the disease from recurring. I was offered two options for maintenance. One, a regular course using common, well-known drugs that may not be effective long-term; two, a special course with expensive drugs. He claimed this could benefit me long-term and raise my testosterone levels to a normal level. It sounds appealing to raise testosterone levels to a normal level. Although it is very low, it can affect memory, cause muscle atrophy, and other unpleasant phenomena. It can also interfere with sexual function.

— ◊ —

I eagerly awaited Dr. Tuck's reply. He didn't rush to reply. Maybe he was tired of me. Perhaps he was too busy with my emails. I hoped that he would reply within one day. Because of the time difference, his work hours were at night and evening. I was able to see that he had actually read my email. (You can request confirmation if your addressee has read your mail.)

Yesterday, I called Dr. Ruthie to complain about my condition and how confusing it was. It was amazing that my PSA reading was zero. However, I was still experiencing aches in my prostate and pelvic areas where large metastases were concentrated. My troubles made her feel depressed. The conversation ended with me agreeing to send her information about Dr. Tuck's treatment method. I did so that night. She was likely busy with her work and other affairs, and did not have the time to get into my details. She didn't expect me to be such a burden when she offered her help as a patient with cancer.

I also lost interest in the dairy. I didn't know my employer. I was not able to cope with the pressure of work, both mentally and physically. On the other hand, I was constantly asking myself: What if I quit? Even worse for a pensioner is the possibility of losing their home.

Slowly, I began to worry about my financial situation. Treatments and drugs kept me spending a lot of money. This was expected to continue, especially if Dr. Tuck gave me the cocktail. As it turned out, I spent many thousands of dollars. I was compelled to ask myself a moral question: How much should I spend on my treatment? Stress set in when I realized that I was gradually eating our savings. I was worried about how I would leave my family with nothing. These were funds that we all wanted to save for our old age and to help our children. But, was it not what we had saved all these years for? We could get through times of distress and crisis? Arieh offered to fund me so that I could enjoy Dr. Tuck's cocktail. I was moved by his gesture. My brother would do anything to help me. However, I don't know if he was a wealthy man with unlimited resources.

— ◊ —

Things weren't moving as fast as we wanted. Today, I received Zomera in the hospital. I also did a PSA test as part of my bloodwork before each treatment. Although it was only a slight difference from the zero result before, the result indicated that my PSA was increasing. My mood was also affected by the awful physical sensations that I felt lately.

Is this a sign that my chemotherapy was ineffective and the ketoconazole treatment wasn't working?

In terms of treatment, I followed Dr. Tuck's instructions and stopped taking ketoconazole or hydrocortisone. After three months, the Zoladex injection's effect also diminished. My new treatment plan included no hormonal treatments and only maintenance therapy. It was an exciting, but daunting experience. Although Dr. Tuck stated that the technique is effective and provides a long-term solution to many problems, what happens if it doesn't work as planned?

Dr. Bassam was kind enough to give me his opinion about Dr. Tuck's suggestion. He was as usual, unaffected by the situation and didn't object. He said, "You can't stop it." He said, "But it will happen again." To make sure I didn't entertain the idea that it could be reversed.

It was quite stressful. Dr. Tuck informed me that my PSA was at 0.2. I asked him whether I should continue with the maintenance treatment. His response was very laconic and he said "YES" in less than an hour. He also asked me to take a testosterone testing along with my next PSA. I was elated by his answer. It gave me more confidence in the path that I was on and would hopefully be the best.

Orr, my firstborn son, was to be drafted into service within one week. This was an extremely stressful time. He was a member of the Nahal Infantry Brigade, and was assigned to the commanders' track. It was difficult to imagine him as an infantry fighter, or as a commander.

My youngest child, Amir was facing more difficulties in his soccer team. His coach didn't include him in the last league game his team played. Every game he missed sent his despair deeper, and after four such games, our child, who was a sweet boy, simply gave up. His parents also broke down.

— ◊ —

My condition was still difficult. I wasn't feeling well. My pelvis and buttocks seemed to be undergoing some unhealthy activity. It was accompanied with a feeling of inertia, fatigue and a sense that I was not moving enough. However, I found that all of the tests I did at that time indicated a stable situation. This was positive. Last PSA result was again zero, while the bone scans and sonograms showed an improvement. Although this was a great improvement, I still felt emotional stress. People around me started to suspect that this was psychological stress, due to the tension I was experiencing. What happens to someone when they lose their mind? I knew it wasn't true based on my instincts. I didn't feel that I was headed towards mental insanity.

Dr. Ruby told me that I had to get rid of the stress. His tone was like someone speaking to someone who is not fully sound. It bothered me a little, so I asked myself if my dark feelings were a result of mental stress.

Trickeries in my soul
Who can relieve me
One day is as black as night

The next is as clear as the sun!

Trickeries in my body
Who can cure me
One day, the pit will be dark

The next is a glimpse of light

— ◊ —

Orr returned from the army to spend the weekend. His new uniform made him happy. He appeared a bit more relaxed and confident in himself. We were glad to see him happy and hoped it would continue that way.

Amir quit the Haifa youth soccer team and returned to play for a local club. Amir seemed to feel lighter from the burden of a difficult task that almost destroyed his mental and physical health. It was also a huge relief for us. He was playing during practice this week, and I enjoyed it. He was a good player and scored a goal.

My condition was still tricking me. On one hand, I felt like the scum was growing inside me again and needed urgent medical attention. My test results showed nothing new. My PSA was still very low at 0.04, the latest test being taken on Wednesday. The CT revealed nothing new and the bone scan showed some improvement.

— ◊ —

Last week, I felt particularly bad. I had a Zomera treatment scheduled on Thursday. I felt sick on Tuesday night and decided to come in before my appointment so Dr. Bassam could discuss it. It felt like my blood was boiling, and I felt a tingling sensation all over my body. It was very bothersome and I couldn't fall asleep. This situation causes the brain to work overtime, adding dark thoughts. My mind saw my end coming and I was about to lose my consciousness. It was a complete-blown "white day." I tore and turned and, despite my earlier decision not to, decided to go on a little "trip". The tiny OxyContin pill, which is a lovely name, allowed me to take it. It allows my mind to completely empty itself until it falls into a sweet stupor. Rivka was available to go with me to the hospital. Although she was surprised by my request, Rivka agreed to accompany me to the hospital. In case the chemotherapy was to be resumed, I carried my Taxotere dose with me. I called the ward to request a reschedule of my appointment for a day earlier. Mimi, the head nursing, was quick to agree. I was familiar with the nurses there. I was young and communicative. They also shared my details about my illness with me, which is something that sets me apart from most patients. I was grateful for their knowledge and dedication, especially Nurse Ann who I almost sex with.

They took my blood and dropped it off at the laboratory. The lab informed me half an hour later that my sample was not suitable for testing and required me to submit a new one. They tried again to needle me, but that didn't go well so they did a third. We sent the sample back to the lab. They returned to us a while later with the same problem. That was code red for me. Mimi explained that it was a technical issue. I asked Mimi if the problem could be due to a blood problem. She hesitated before answering that she didn't think so. My suspicion was raised by her hesitation when she said that there might be a problem with my blood. Rivka also shared my concern. It was almost like she got anxious too. The results were finally in after a while. False alarm, everything was fine. Dr. Bassam welcomed us into his office to discuss our situation. The discussion was thorough unlike previous ones. He looked at the CT images and stated that he didn't see any change. Although the PSA reading was very high at 0.04, I was still bothered and concerned by the tingling sensations and the blood boiling sensation. Dr. Bassam stated that treatment is based on facts and not on sensations. It was decided that nothing should be changed at this time. He suggested that it could be mental. I was close to being convinced. I was almost convinced.

Rivka left. I was able to continue my Zomera treatment at the hospital. Nurse Ann was attentive to my situation and I was able to share my feelings with her. To help me gain insight, she used all her experience and knowledge. After I was done with the treatment, I realized that I hadn't taken the Taxotere medication I brought to the hospital.

I called Nurse Ann the next day. I explained to her that I had lost the Taxotere, and she promised to keep it. I answered so-so when she asked me about my health. She was also curious to know what Dr. Tuck thought about the matter. I replied that he didn't know what to do. I shared with her the letter he wrote about hypercalcemia. It was due to prolonged Zomera use and an excess of calcium in the body. Extra calcium can cause liver damage, liver failure, and even death. Recently, I felt a lot better and stopped taking my calcium dosage. Ann went to see Dr. Bassam about the matter. I promised her that I would call her back the next day to get his reply. I was contacted by Ann an hour later. She informed me that my calcium test results had been slightly off, but that they believed there could be a shortage or surplus of magnesium. Ann sent me to check the magnesium levels in my blood. To check for hypercalcemia, I had to have a urine test.

I was required to give blood at the clinic. I was given a 3-liter (101-ounces) container to use for the next 24 hours. They also instructed me to return the container the next day. I hoped the cause of my negative feelings would be revealed and that we would find out what was happening. Surprisingly, each day passed and I felt better. I believe it was related to my stopping taking my calcium supplement.

— ◊ —

Recently, my desire to leave the dairy was a constant concern. It felt like I was not getting any benefit from my job there. I couldn't exert any effort and lost the joy of creativity. I lost the joy of getting up each morning to go to work.

Dror was my partner. He didn't believe that I was serious at first. He kept asking me what I would do at my home. It was a question I had been thinking about for a while, but I didn't have the answer. Maybe I should look for a suitable occupation for a pensioner. Why not? I knew I could find a good job, even though I was in poor health. I had to find a lunatic to buy my share. Dror stated that he wouldn't agree to be a partner with anyone. It would be difficult for him to "fall deeply in love" with someone else. My brother Arieh had an acquaintance who asked me about the dairy business. I asked him to verify with the man if he was interested buying my share of the dairy. Our accountant was also present to help us appraise the dairy's worth, which is important information should we decide to enter into negotiations to sell our share.

It wasn't easy to end this partnership.

— ◊ —

Saturday was extremely rainy. Our TV satellite dish on our roof had been damaged by a storm. Orr was available to help restore the dish, but he was away on leave from the Army and left with his friends. Although he promised to be back soon, I doubt if he will keep his word. I didn't want to make him feel too burdened.

All my tests had been fine except for the low white blood cells count. Although the doctors claimed it was nothing, I wasn't convinced. My physical symptoms were too severe and lasted longer than doctors' words. Friday was my second visit to Dr. Bassam. I actually forced myself on him, and even apologized. He took a look at me and even put a finger on my back. Despite my nagging sensations, he believed there was no need to do anything else. He didn't like changes, I knew. He wouldn't change anything unless I told him exactly what I wanted, even if that meant I was dead in his arms.

Avivit made an appointment for Monday. Avivit is open-minded and has a lot knowledge. With her help, I hope we can reach a logical conclusion.

Another week passed. My physical condition was not improving. All over my body, I felt tingling and itching. Someone once said it was a sign of terminal dispersion. It was a feeling that I felt, like my soul was leaving my body. There was nothing I could do to stop it. It felt as if I was losing my life, and that I was being taken out of the loop.

Rivka asked me what the essence of the feeling was. I replied that it was the deepest sorrow at the impending loss of life. It left behind an entire fabric that could not have ended naturally, as one would expect. It was particularly difficult for me to leave my kids behind. It was obvious that single-parent families had low social ratings and that each family member would be subject to heavy social penalties.

It was also difficult for me to see Orr in the army. It would be difficult for him to deal with it alone. And what if - God forbid - something bad happens to him? What would his family do?

Amir was also a concern of mine. He was extremely sensitive. It was a huge crisis for him and I didn't know how he would overcome it.

Bat-El was strong, but introverted. She would probably find a way for her to manage herself in times of crisis.

—— ◊ ——

Avivit met me on Monday. Ruthie had already sent me Dr. Tuck's recommendations so that she could review them. It was a pleasant surprise to see her calmer and less stressed. Avivit didn't have anything new to say. Avivit resentfully objected to Dr. Tuck's suggestion to artificially raise my testosterone. It was crazy, she thought. Because I respect her as a professional, and I felt the same way, Dr. Tuck's suggestion was unambiguous. Avivit suggested that I try strontium-89 radioactive substance, which is designed to reduce pain in the bones. Side effect is the long-term negative effect it has on your immune system. Given my history and the fact that I have an aggressive disease, this treatment does not work for me for at least two to three months. I also did not experience any bone pain. This recommendation doesn't resonate with me. Avivit didn't have any other words to share. We parted ways with mixed feelings. Although she did suggest a method of operation, the overall atmosphere only reinforced my sense of despair at the end of the road.

On Wednesday, I was back in the hospital. I informed Dr. Bassam of my current condition and asked him to give the Zoladex. He agreed and explained to the nurses how to give the injection. I didn't need to hear anything more.

Itching and tingling continued. Avivit called me again to inquire if she thought I should resume chemotherapy. It would not work and she reiterated her recommendation to take the strontium shots.

After a long time, I decided to resume chemo. I arrived at Dr. Bassam's office on Monday, December 30 2002 and began a new round.

After two to three days, the chemo had a positive effect. However, itching and tingling returned. It started slowly increasing in volume but then it decreased to a lower level. These bastard cells were floating around my body, bothering me and against my will, but it seemed like nothing could affect them. Even worse, it was torturing me!

It was a week that passed quickly. I arrived at chemo feeling relieved to have my weekly dose of poison. This allowed me to continue to work. Inside, I felt disappointed. I was headed towards failure, despite all my efforts. The forum shows that patients with my condition and the most intelligent survived for about five years. In my case, however, I had been dead walking for fifteen months. Despite all my efforts to understand and treat the disease and my attempts at taking an unconventional approach to the problem, did I lose the battle sooner than I expected?

CHAPTER TEN

"THE NEWCASTLE":

NEWCASTLE TREATMENT and INSTALLATION OF THE PORT

January to the End of April 2003

Amram, my cousin who lives in Jerusalem's Golan Heights, was being seen by a Jerusalem doctor to treat his high blood pressure. Two years ago, he had suffered a minor heart attack. This doctor was injecting a substance into his bloodstream to remove any residual. He mentioned my name to his doctor, and he said that he had something for me. Amram called me to inform me that the doctor would offer me a virus injection of Newcastle disease. This is a viral epidemic that typically attacks chickens. We used to immunize our chickens against the virus when we were children. The theory that the virus can only settle in cancerous cells within the human body and then spreads to other parts of the body until it kills them has been developed over time. It does not harm healthy cells. Although the technique for using this virus has been around for approximately fifty years, its application was only recently discovered.

An internet story featured a story about a European farmer suffering from prostate cancer. His chickens were infected with Newcastle disease. He went to their coop to treat the disease that had infected his chickens. But, lo and behold, the cancer was gone a little later. It was either a true story, or a fairy tale, and I didn't know if it had anything to do the development of the drug for patients with cancer.

We met the doctor in Jerusalem. He was a religious man who saw patients at his home. It was an old-fashioned house with an old-fashioned spouse. Our sages' essays were plastered on the walls, while holy books were stored in the bookcase. He informed us that Professor F, a professor at Hadassah Hospital Jerusalem, was running an organized trial for this vaccine. Before I decided to go this route, I knew I had to meet the professor.

I had done some research online and spoke with Avivit and Dr.

Bassam. Avivit advised me to get off my high horse. Avivit claimed she had witnessed patients with my condition contract Newcastle disease due to a weak immune system.

Dr. Bassam did not add any new information, but he said, "Listen. It's all experimental." He also stated that he didn't know much about the subject, so he could do what s/he wanted. I believe I was exhausting him by all my "innovations." They were his top priority. He did not use avantgarde treatment, just like other oncologists.

We drove back to Jerusalem to meet Professor F. He was a kind man and gave us an hour of our time free of charge. He was an expert in this field, which I discovered. Although he didn't explicitly state it, his attitude towards the matter was positive. It was still experimental. Irit described it as follows: "Since experts have determined that there is no risk to your health, and there is a chance it might help you, then aside the large expense, it is worth taking a chance." I agreed and decided to take it.

His wife was his right hand and filled out the forms. She then sent them to the American vaccine manufacturer. I would receive a dosage recommendation, instructions, and an invoice within two to three working days. I was to get the substance from a woman whose daughter had used it for brain cancer treatment for six years. Her mother believed that she was the one who saved her life.

I received the dose from the U.S. manufacturer a few days later along with the instructions and, not less important, the invoice. The "initiation fees" of three thousand dollars were paid upfront. They also included $15 for a regular shot, and $60 for an additional strength shot. Three regular shots and two extra-strength shots were recommended per week. The initiation fees were approximately $800 per month. It's a great deal for a small amount of nickels and dimes!

This "factory"' marketing director was an American lady named Eva Chatary. It seemed like a family-owned business because it was created in Hungary by another doctor named Chatary. I talked with her and we agreed to split the $3,000 initiation fee into three $1,000 payments. I sent her the first payment. We drove back to Jerusalem the following day and Mazal gave me the substance for the next month. We then went to the doctor to receive our first injection. The shot was prepared by the doctor. I was able to notice that the doctor had not added the virus to the sterilized water and made a comment. He would have infused me with only sterile water if I hadn't noticed. After much preparation, he finally injected the substance into me. I felt both excited and curious. Is it going to make a big difference in my life?

After the injection, we drove home, went to Izhar, Irit, and had dinner. It was a good feeling. Itching and tingling subsided. I felt a wave of optimism. Rivka and I shared our joy, and it was cause for celebration. Rivka is a tireless supporter of me and my journey, and she will do anything for me. She finds a way for me to have the intimate physical connection I long for at night.

Tonight, I explained to her that my father moved into the next room after my mother died from cancer. As if a woman with her condition didn't need support and intimacy. He had probably developed a severe infection in his leg. Perhaps he was afraid of hurting her. Rivka stated that my father was well-known for his insensitivity.

Five times per week, the new drug must be injected into the vein. Although I assumed that our neighbor, a hospital nurse, could inject it for us, to my surprise, she told me that nurses are not permitted to inject into the vein. I inquired about her reasoning. After all, I was receiving IV to my vein treatments from nurses. She explained that this was done under the supervision and oversight of oncologists even though they weren't physically present in the treatment area.

I asked Dr. Nabil what he thought was the best way to overcome this obstacle. Dr. Nabil agreed to help me. I was fortunate to have doctors who were supportive and able to cater to my every need.

Now I was at Dr. Nabil Hatib's house to get my daily Newcastle dose. We drove to his house, and he would inject the drug into me vein. It was forty minutes later that we were back home.

It was a reasonable procedure. Only the itching and tingling had returned to some extent and my feeling of euphoria wasn't too early.

It was to be seen if I would die sooner or later.

The injections into the vein became more complicated. My veins were buried deep in my flesh.

This is common among patients undergoing chemotherapy or other treatments. It is becoming increasingly difficult to insert needles in the veins for IV purposes, or for drawing blood.

It was so bad that it made it nearly impossible to insert an IV needle. Multiple attempts at finding a vein required much prodding and poking into the flesh. Each of these attempts was pure torture.

It was my only choice so I decided, along with my medical advisors, to install a Porta-Cath (or port).

INSTALLING THE PORT

A flexible plastic tube is used to install the port. It is inserted under the skin and threaded onto the artery that transports blood from the heart. The tube's other end is connected to the bottom of a small tin can of stainless steel. It's about the same size as a button in diameter and has four buttons in height. The entire set-up is placed under the skin on the one side of your chest. Because the can is cylindrical, the IV needle can penetrate the plastic material. This makes it easier to inject fluid into the tube that connects to the artery. The port must be installed under partial anesthesia.

This option was something I had seen on an internet forum. Ann demonstrated how to inject IV through a port into a patient with this setup. He gave his consent. I discussed it with Dr. Bassam, who supported the installation and gave his approval. The date was set and I was transferred to hospital in my blue and white pajamas. I was again parked at the entry to the operating room. It took a while to get blankets. As I lay on my back, facing the ceiling, thoughts flooded my mind, and I felt alone.

I was thinking about how someone I didn't know was going to cut me and insert a tube into my artery which carried blood from my heart. Someone I didn't know anything about. Did I submit myself once again to the mercy of another? Did the surgeon know that I was a cancer-patient? If so, did it affect his work? He made less effort as the patient would not live long enough to justify investing his time. He was astonished at my suspicions and assured me he would do his best. As my thoughts raced, I was informed by the surgeon that the only incision would be made in the area where the ports would be placed. It was a miracle. He asked me if I had ever driven a car. I answered yes. He suggested that I install the can on my left side, so that my seatbelt would not be pressed against it while I was in the driver's chair. The idea was appealing to me so I agreed. I was then given a shot, and my consciousness disappeared within a matter of seconds. Although I could hear and see something happening in the background, it felt as if it were happening to someone else.

The port was installed when I awoke later. I was told everything was fine and that my first IV could be administered through the port the following day. This seemed strange to me. It was possible to get IV through the port as soon as tomorrow. How about the stitches? It sounded almost like a machine you could activate immediately after it was installed.

Rivka came to pick me up. I was glad to see her. I was irritated by the pain and took painkillers. The pain continued for a few days. Although the pain in my chest was most severe during the first few nights following the installation, it was not as severe or painful as the irritations that I was already used to. The only thing you could see from the outside was the bulge in the can beneath the skin. It was the button side, and was located on my right chest.

It took me a while before I was able to receive an IV through the new port. Because I didn't know how the new system would work, I was anxious.

To prevent infection, sterilize the area around the IV three times. Next, the port needle is inserted into the skin through the plastic material in the can. The port needle's external end is connected to a flexible tube measuring approximately 20 cm in length. This tube allows for the attachment of an IV bag standard or a syringe to allow for injections or blood-drawing.

Once the needle has been inserted into the port the blood is then pumped from the port with a syringe. Because the blood inside the port's tube does not flow naturally, it is kept there and could congeal. These blood clots can be transmitted into the bloodstream by administering an IV without drawing blood through the tube.

A blood clot can block a blood vessel, causing thrombosis. It can be fatal if the blood clot is found in the bloodstream, heart, lungs or brain.

The entire system is then cleaned with sterile cleaning water that is poured into your bloodstream. This cleaning is done to make sure that the system is working properly and there are no obstructions in the tubes. This is a plumbing marvel. The bag containing the actual substance (Zomera, in my case), is then hooked. To prevent any residual substance from getting into the tubes, the tubes must be cleaned once more. The final step involves injecting a blood thinner called Heparin. This fills the tubes to the exact size so that no blood from the patient can flow in. This is another way to prevent blood clots forming between the current treatment and the next. This completes the measures to prevent blood clots from forming due to port usage.

Port use is a risky business.

One of my treatments was a mistake. The nurse who attended me didn't draw blood as instructed in the beginning, but instead went straight to cleansing. It was too late for me to stop this. I panicked. I was worried about a blood clot getting into my bloodstream. It didn't happen. Mimi, the head nurse in the treatment room, was not amused. I demanded that the nurse stop my treatments. Mimi and the nurse both apologized and promised to never do it again. Today, that nurse administered my IVs to me. She is no longer prone to making mistakes. She makes sure that she draws blood before hooking up the IV.

So that I wouldn't have to visit Dr. Nabil every day, I began to prepare a kit to inject the Newcastle at my home. It was quite a difficult task. Ann connected the needle to my chest port. A plastic tube measuring 20 cm in length was attached to the needle's tip. It could be used to connect to an IV or syringe. I carried it around under my shirt as it was hanging from my body. This construction was fastened to my chest with a special patch. The tube and needle that was hanging from it had to be changed every other week, which took up to ten days. The array that was hanging from my body was very bothersome. It was also important to avoid infections.

Sets for self-injection were prepared by me. They included sterilizers, syringes and cleansing water. Although I was initially tempted to get them from the hospital, I soon felt ashamed and asked for favors. To overcome this bureaucratic obstacle, I turned to the Ma'alot health clinic. Without any notice, I started to receive medical supplies that I needed for this treatment. Amazingly, they allowed me to receive a large quantity of medical supplies for injections, and also organized transportation to deliver this supply to my home. The saying goes, "God works mysteriously."

It was complex and delicate to inject the drug. First, I had draw my blood. Then, I had sterile water to clean the needle and then inject the drug. To complete the procedure, I had a second wash with soap and water. I then filled the tube with 5 cubic cms of blood thinner to prevent blood clots. This procedure is very important. Rivka was a great help the first time. As we attempted this first time, our hands shaken. We were to be very careful not to make a mistake. I was able to do the procedure by myself later. It was much more easy than I thought.

Eva Chatary called me. The doctor's wife wanted to know my feelings. He was aware that I was receiving chemotherapy simultaneously to my Newcastle treatment. He was very interested in the combination of both. I didn't have any insight to share. My legs had swollen a bit, but that was all I could say.

January 28, 2003 was an election day. It was a cold day. We were home. I went to Mitzpe Hila to vote. It was refreshing to get out. I was tired of the endless inactivity. I tried to imagine how it would feel if I quit the dairy. We were in negotiations with potential buyers but they didn't seem willing to pay the amount we asked. Therefore, it was unlikely that anything would happen. Having my ability to work was so compromised, I couldn't continue running the business. This was a real problem.

I continued to take the Newcastle and continued the chemotherapy. Sometimes I felt that this combination was working. Other times, I felt like something was wrong.

I didn't know if I would make it to the election day so I kept checking off little achievements. My next goal was to make it in one piece to Orr's end-of-basic-training swearing-in ceremony at the Western Wall the following Thursday, February 6. My horizon was steadily expanding. I was working on it slowly, marking my goals as within reach and taking it one day at a time. It was a small accomplishment that allowed me to maintain some sanity, and also helped me be optimistic when I conquered them.

— ◊ —

On Thursday, Orr was sworn-in in the army. Because I was feeling good lately and wanted to be there, I decided to delay my chemo treatment from Thursday to Sunday. I didn't want my son to feel that he couldn't come because his father was disabled. It turned out that life wasn't so easy. After walking around in the cold, I developed a severe case of the common cold. My immune system was weak so I had to take precautions to avoid getting a cold or an infection. However, knowledge was not enough. You had to act upon it.

The ceremony was originally planned for Jerusalem's Western Wall, but budgetary constraints forced it to be held close to the base. This is a long drive for anyone, not just a bag of bones like myself. On the way, I could feel my body getting achy.

The ceremony was typical of the army: chaotic with many soldiers and more guests. We were pleased to see that the soldiers were released immediately after the ceremony. We drove the "kid" to Jerusalem and stayed at Izhar's. Zivit and Nitzan, my cousins, came to visit us at Izhar. Despite my poor health, they put us in a good mood. They made us laugh and had fun. We drove to my supplier the next morning to pick up my second Newcastle batch. However, she didn't have enough of the full quantity that I ordered. She had five bottles less of the extra-strong Newcastle. To get the rest of the drug, we would need to make arrangements. When we arrived home, I felt sick. It was a mild case of the common cold this time.

Initial signs indicated that my condition was improving. I felt a bit better and the nagging sensations became less annoying, which was encouraging. With the illness I was dealt, it is possible for anything to change in a matter of minutes and there is no way to know what the future holds. However, I did feel something positive. Let it go on like this. Avivit stated that she had nothing to offer me two months ago and that I should do what I think is best. It was worth living to prove that to Avivit.

This illness is multifaceted and deceiving, so I'm going to add a condition to my words. One aspect could improve while another facet is facing problems. You never know which direction the wind will blow.

Along with my progress, there were also other factors that led me to the bottom. One of the most irritating phenomena is what I refer to as "birds in an puddle". I felt a shaking sensation under my skin. It was similar to a bird shaking off water after bathing. It was not a common phenomenon. I tried to ask Dr. Bassam about it, but he didn't know what I meant. A second side effect of prolonged chemotherapy is peripheral Neuropathy. This is a condition where the peripheral nerves in your arms and legs are not controlled, causing numbing. It's like thousands of ants crawling on your arms, legs and hands. It is under the skin and can't be reversed. It has not been reported in the same degree by me.

I knew I couldn't keep winning with chemotherapy forever. It was time to end it with all its implications. I could either do without the chemotherapy or not. The situation was difficult and grim, regardless of my optimism.

Yesterday, February 20, 2003, was the last day of my chemotherapy. Although I felt relieved, I was still afraid of what might happen if the scum attacks me again.

It was getting warmer. My chest was covered in sweat. It didn't look or smell right. The needle was inserted through my body during the summer and I couldn't continue. I was afraid of infection. Three months after I started using Newcastle, I decided to stop using it. I didn't know how much this treatment had helped me fight this scum. Ann took the needle out of my body and I sighed in relief.

Recent developments have been dramatic. My younger brother, Izhar, was diagnosed with prostate cancer. We are a "prone family" so he was carefully examined and diagnosed with the disease. We were happy to learn that he was diagnosed at an early stage. His prostate was removed and he was expected to fully recover. We visited him at the hospital. He said that he had been saved by me. He was most likely right. My diagnosis would have prevented his disease from being detected. It was not in such a critical stage. I was overwhelmed with envy. This led me to feel a lot of guilt. If I had been more determined to see the signs, and had taken the time to understand the signs and performed the tests, I could have been a healthier man, or at least close to it today. I was instead dragging my feet down this horrible path. Even though I had been seeing a doctor for over a year before I was diagnosed, it was still a long way to go. If I had been diagnosed one year earlier, I might have been healthy or mildly ill today. I foolishly followed his example and dismissed him with the explicit statement that he was healthy.

CHAPTER ELEVEN

THE SECOND CHEMOTHERAPY PROTOCOL

May to Mid- August 2003

After another chemotherapy treatment the day before, I was back at home. Logothetis, the doctor who created it, was the name of the new protocol. Two weeks ago I started the protocol. I was tired but I found that my desire to write outweighed my fatigue. Although I wasn't sure what or who I was writing about, I felt compelled to keep going. After I finished checking out, I wondered if anyone would read my journal. It would move someone. It would move anyone? This is what engineers call a "pressure-relieving valve".

Rivka and myself met with Dr. Ace and I met to discuss the next steps. He asked me about my pain. He suggested another protocol for chemo that had shown promising results in clinical trials. The protocol's name was inspired by the Logothetis doctor who created it. This protocol was a favorite of mine, if you can ever like a chemo protocol. It contained two chemo drugs as well as other proven anticancer medications. The combination of several drugs can create a powerful synergetic effect that makes them more effective together than when they are used separately. Similar to the first chemo protocol it was based on a weekly treatment followed by a break after several treatments. Even though my PSA was still zero, we decided that it would be worth the risk and give the cancer another shot.

Dr. Ace informed me that chemo can cause total hair loss. To avoid dramatic changes in my appearance, I decided to go bald. Before I started the chemotherapy, I visited the hairdresser to request that he shave my head. I was happy with the results when I looked into the mirror. It would have made it much easier for me to endure this painful treatment.

After we left the doctor, I was optimistic for a second, with the Jewish resistance song from World War II playing in the background, its words echoing my current state. Rivka was amused by my lyrical talents as I sang it in my car on the return trip:

Do not think that this is your final path.

Although leaden skies can cover more days of blue than the rest,.
The hour we have longed for is near.

Our step is stronger than the message: "We're here!"

— ◊ —

Logothetis began for me more than two weeks ago. The combination of chemotherapy drugs was meant to suppress the scum for quite a while. After carefully studying the protocol, I realized that I did not follow all of its recommendations. I was not a candidate for this recommendation. Estracyt was also included in the protocol. I had taken it before. It was not clear if it would be of any benefit to me again.

This is the most important rule for dealing with this scum: if you've used a drug before, it has "burnt". Next time you use it, it will likely not affect you as much.

My medical stats at the time I started treatment were positive. My PSA was close to zero which indicated that the disease was at a lull. This was an important circumstance that contributed to the success of the treatment, despite its limitations.

My blood work before the second treatment revealed a low white blood count. This was so low that my immune system was considered borderline. This means that I wouldn't be able receive more chemotherapy if my count dropped further. A drop in my blood counts could put me at risk of losing my life. Additionally, I was becoming very weak due to the treatment.

The body's resistance to infection and strength is determined by the number of white blood cell in its blood. If the number of white cells in our blood drops, we can be susceptible to many diseases.

The immune system is weakened and white cell count decreases after chemotherapy. To allow the immune system to heal, chemotherapy should be stopped in extreme cases.

I was in a severe emotional crisis because of this condition. I was unable to stop moving around the house and didn't know what to do. Rivka was the one who suffered most from my mood swings. She did her best to listen and offer practical suggestions. Most of these were intended to improve my emotional and physical well-being. I was able to go out and forget about the problem. Partly because some of her suggestions were not appealing to me, and others were more physically demanding, I wasn't always open to them. Rivka suggested that I look into new treatment options, something with which I had problems as well. With all the information I had, I realized that no one could offer me any secrets. Did I lose the faith that I had in my ability to overcome this scum? It felt like my inner energy was dwindling and I had no choice but to give up. We didn't have any great ideas.

My family wanted to spend as much time as possible with us. Dina, Arieh and my father visited last evening. We enjoyed a wonderful time sitting on the porch and eating watermelon with goat's milk cheese. My father wanted to know more about the workings and benefits of the internet. My father had been asking me for help with the internet for some time. I failed to convince him. He has always struggled to understand technical matters. The internet was something he could never comprehend. He needed an orthotic belt to protect his back. I taught him how to find one online. I don't know if my efforts were successful in sparked his interest. When I asked him if details about the suppliers we had found online, he replied "No, no." I will discuss this with my orthopedist."

Irit and Izhar were also paying attention to me. Izhar called me every 2 to 3 days and sent me emails with all the relevant information to my condition. Irit sent me a heartfelt email. It appears at the end.

I did not go to work today because my blood count dropped significantly. You could say I was below the red line. It meant that my immune system was not protecting me at the moment from any ailments, and I could contract any germs around. Therefore, I had to be careful when coming into contact with people, especially sick ones, and not be in places crawling with germs, like the dairy. Dr. Ruthie, as well as Dr. Nabil, had warned me of it. The other problem was that I could not continue the chemo in such condition, which made things even worse. This mess put me in a vulnerable emotional state, unable to control my tear sac, and the tears flew freely at any occasion, making me self-conscious every time. But it was no surprise, really. The feeling that everything was closing in on me was terrible and unimaginable, pulling me into a state of deep depression.

Sometimes I was overwhelmed by suicidal thoughts, wondering how I could get rid of this verdict. I tried to help myself using spiritual techniques. I used guided imagery, trying to convince the systems in my body to eradicate the monster. It required emotional strength and concentration, but provided a pleasant illusion of well-being in the body at least for some time.

— ◊ —

On Sunday, Izhar and Irit came to visit and stayed until Monday afternoon. They arrived late as usual, after some event in Tel Aviv. We sat down that evening and carried on an intellectual conversation that reminded me somewhat of my father's conversations with his brothers more than twenty years ago. They could argue heatedly, for an hour or more, about a line written by a Polish poet in the nineteenth century. These types of conversations had no insight or conclusion. But it was fun. The next morning, I went in for some tests at our local health clinic. I asked Dr. Nabil to prescribe me something moderate for sleep, since I have been suffering from insomnia lately. On the way back, I picked up the prescription drug from the pharmacy.

There was a Russian grocery store near the pharmacy, where I liked to buy various Russian foods, especially pickled herring. I bought a few items at the delicatessen and went home. We prepared breakfast with Izhar and Irit, devouring the treats, since we were very hungry by then. Rivka came home from work later. We sat in the front yard; Irit pulled out her video camera and filmed me mainly. We spoke about the cancer issues that have been constantly preoccupying me. When I tried to express my feelings, the tears welled up again.

"My problem," I tried to explain, "is the lack of hope. It makes the situation that much harder."

Izhar said he had also felt this way before his operation, when he was convinced the cancer had spread into his stomach.

I felt pretty good the following day, until the old blood count issue came up again, flooding me with all the negative emotions and sense of a dead end.

— ◊ —

I was in touch with Dr. Charles Myers by email. He was one of the biggest experts in the United States. I knew of his expertise since he participated and expressed his opinions in the patients' forum every so often. After sending him a summary of my medical condition, I asked him if there was any treatment he could recommend to me. He asked me to take some additional tests so he has a better idea of my current state. Only then, he said, would he know if he had any "news" for me. I did some of the tests so far. He asked for a bone scan and a CT, which I had already done last March. I knew these tests involve extensive radiation to the body and could cause problems in the future, so I was debating whether I should repeat them.

I called Avivit today about my blood count results. In her sharp tone, she ordered me to stop the chemotherapy and the Nizoral at once. Nizoral was one of the supporting drugs on the protocol that may damage liver functions. Her words were clear-cut and simple: "We both know you're going to die, and if you continue to take Nizoral or chemo, your liver will fail within a short amount of time, whereas if you stop now, you have another two years to live."

I knew that only Avivit was capable of uttering such brutal words. And I? What did I do with myself in a moment like this? I "escaped" through my emergency exit intended for moments like these, and detached myself, as if she were talking about someone else. Let her say whatever she wanted and I will continue on my path.

The main chemo drug was called Adriamycin. It seemed to be the main hurdle. One of its leading side effects was damage to the myocardium due to prolonged use. In order to find out if damage was indeed done to the myocardium, I agreed with Dr. Bassam to take an echocardiogram after every two chemo treatments.

Echocardiogram is a heart sonogram that clearly and colorfully displays an image of the heart and its functioning on a computer screen.

I befriended the doctor who examined my heart chambers and showed me during each sonogram how the valves worked, opening and closing, a true miracle. Luckily, no decline in the myocardium functioning was detected during this protocol.

This chemo was beating me down. It was no doubt harsher than the first chemo protocol. Luckily, it was done in rounds of four treatments with a four-week break. Then another four weeks of chemo, but with a different drug. During the break, I had to swallow different types of pills that were meant to preserve the situation, so that the cancer would not take advantage of the opportunity to gather more strength. I was also supposed to receive an injection with the radioactive substance strontium-89.

In five days, I am completing my first round of chemo. Now I look like a "real" cancer patient. I look in the mirror and I can hardly recognize myself. My cheeks are sunken, I lost my hair, even chest and armpit hair, and I am not myself.

There are other side effects a healthy person does not face. Fatigue is among the worst. It turns me into a rag doll. It is so powerful in the morning that I have no energy to get out of bed. And it lasts throughout the day. I drag myself to the dairy, going to the office everyday and hardly accomplishing anything. I am a shadow of myself. You can tell I am depressed. Even my friend Lenny, who saw how my depression was progressing, told me I should take my own life. Just like that.

I am halfway through. I am now on a four-week hiatus from the chemo. According to plan, I received my strontium-89 radioactive injection yesterday.

Strontium-89 (Sr-89) along with strontium-90, are the outcome of splitting uranium 235 and plutonium 239, which radiates beta rays. It takes 50.5 days for its radiation power to decrease by half from its original intensity.

Obtaining the approval for the strontium-89 shot required great bureaucratic effort, as it involved a special permission. It seems that this substance is pretty expensive and is not given to many patients. A few weeks ago, we approached the health clinic with an official request legally signed by the oncologist. But for some reason, they did not approve the injection. I got the impression that the clinic was trying to avoid giving permission. I did not delve too deeply into the circumstances, but after some nagging and Dr. Nabil's intervention, I finally obtained the approval.

The injection itself was administered at the outpatient clinic of the Haifa hospital. I guess there was no one authorized to administer this drug at the Nahariya hospital.

The outpatient clinic in Haifa is not as nice and intimate as the one I am used to in Nahariya. The waiting room is crowded with many patients, some who look quite sick. None of the medical staff is in sight. Every so often, the loudspeaker calls out the name of one of the waiting patients, referring them to a certain room number. The long wait was hard for me. I was nervous. I wanted to go out and get some fresh air, but I was afraid I would not hear when they called me in for the injection.

I was finally summoned to one of the rooms. A doctor and a nurse met me there. After filling out a form with my details, they began the preparations. It is not an ordinary injection. It must be administered by an authorized doctor. Since it is a radioactive substance, the special container it is kept in, as well as the syringe, are designed so as not to allow any radiation emission. Seeing how many steps are taken to ensure that no radiation is emitted before the substance is injected into my body, I wonder what kind of damage it will do inside me. The nurse tightened the band across my arm to slow down the flow of blood in the veins so they would pop. The doctor inserted the needle gently into the vein on the back of my palm. She drew some blood to make sure that needle was properly inserted. I was pleased and so was she, to see blood coming out. The radioactive substance is finally injected into my body. I waited a few minutes to see that I was fine and then stepped out of the clinic into a warm summer day, sighing in relief. I noted that I did not feel any different as a "radioactive" man.

Avivit advised me to take precautions for two weeks following the injection. Especially, to use different bathrooms than the rest of the family, because radioactive residue is eliminated through bodily secretions. She also recommended to wash my laundry separately. I explained the new instructions to my family, and they designated the bathroom closest to my bedroom as mine to use. I feel a little bit like a leper.

Yesterday, something unprecedented happened. My chemo was cancelled due to a low blood count. When the blood count is so low, the immune system is weakens and the risk of contracting any type of infection or ailment is very high.

Ann suggested I use a mask over my face. I did. It felt like I was bearing the mark of Cain on my forehead. Everyone would know I was severely ill. I could not bear the sight of myself with the mask, so I took it off a few minutes later and drove home.

— ◊ —

Today was a festive day for me. Yesterday, I finally completed Dr. Logothetis's protocol. The treatment was possible after my blood counts improved. It was the last one in a series of four last treatments.

With Dr. Bassam's consent, we decreased the chemo drug by a third during this last series. I had felt, and you could tell when looking at me, that the dose of chemo drugs shoved into my body was too intense. My body was on the verge of a breakdown. My red and white blood cells, as well as my hemoglobin, were low.

Reducing the chemo drug dose was a real lifesaver for me. I was ready to collapse. Even now, my general condition was still shaky. I hoped it would improve in the coming days, but I was trying not to think about the far future so I could invest the little energy I had in recovering from this hurdle. I prayed this agonizing treatment was truly another blow to the scum and would add to my battle against it.

— ◊ —

I was happy to meet Ann each time I arrived at the treatment room in the oncological ward. When she treated me, I felt like I was in good hands. Her pretty face always radiated with a smile. I admired her ability and willingness to discuss medical matters that were concerning me and also her beneficial advice. I also liked her sense of humor and rolling laughter when I called her Sister Ann. To me, she was the ideal nurse, both as a professional and as a human being.

Ann dressed up as an angel for Purim[10]. She wore white angel wings on her white nurse coat. I told her, and I meant it, that she was the white angel not just on Purim but all year round. When the treatment room administration changed, I asked Ann why she was not appointed head nurse. She seemed most suitable to me. She did not give a clear answer.

Ann's care and amicable relationships with the patients was not positively viewed by the ward's administration. They claimed she was not quick enough and thus inefficient in the number of patients she handled. They said she chatted with them too much—God forbid! I did not know about all of this.

One day, when I arrived for a treatment, Ann was simply gone. Another nurse was placed in charge of me. Her caretaking was professional and devoted, but lacked the perks I would get with Ann. After inquiring about it, I found out that Ann was transferred to the oncological inpatient ward, where she was appointed head nurse. Later on, I heard that she did not stay there long either. She was transferred to the maternity ward. I guess she was too good for them, too.

Did the system see what I saw? Are the exceptional ways destined to be ousted? I hope not, but it seemed to be the case with Ann. I never called her since, and to this day, I feel guilty about it. She helped me so much in my darkest hours, and I did not even bother to pick up the phone and call her.

Irit Gal's Letter

It is after midnight. We are listening to Latin music, which, as always, conveys joy, sadness, beauty, and much longing. Izhar is busy writing, so I thought I would write you something. We think about you often, and how this unfortunate situation of trying to preserve life requires so much effort, asking you to make crucial decisions on a daily basis.

Sometimes your younger brother, Izhar, whose soul is intertwined with yours, talks about his desire to pull you from all of this into a motorcycle trip or to one of those destinations so many dream of reaching but so few do. To put aside these messy genetics—the same ones that have awarded you both with such beautiful, blue eyes.

When I had just met Izhar, I was offended by him and kicked him jokingly, but unintentionally, my kick landed right where his knee had been fractured once. He winced and grabbed his leg, then said something that has stayed with me ever since: "Can we accept the good without accepting the bad?" And hugged me instead of being mad.

Why am I bringing this up? Because alongside the bad that you are both going through, especially you, there is the quiet good. Good like the love between two brothers, who once used to fight like two roosters, and today dip Newcastle in ice.

Hope we meet soon to talk, listen, and film.

See you soon,
Irit

---

10 A Jewish holiday that commemorates the saving of the Jews from the Persian king's decree as recorded in the Book of Esther. One of the holiday's customs is to wear costumes and celebrate by feasting.

CHAPTER TWELVE

HOW WE DIDN'T TRANSPLANT BONE MARROW

September 2003

Was I doing everything I could to cope with my cancer? Was I not resting in the warm bosom of my blood test results? My PSA showed an ongoing zero result, which is all I could ask for, but I felt restless. I constantly felt the need to keep hitting the scum over the head in "**the way of the cat**"as steadily as possible.

My nephew, Yoav, told me about a friend's father who had severe skin melanoma and was on his deathbed. He had undergone bone marrow transplant and recovered, so they said. I wondered, *perhaps there is a new option we have not yet considered? Could this be of interest to us? It is worth checking out.*

We began to look into this option. We found out that the expert on the matter was Dr. S, the head of the bone marrow transplant unit at a hospital in
Jerusalem. We traveled to meet him—my devoted wife Rivka, my brother Izhar, and I.

The doctor explained the various transplant techniques and we understood that thus far, transplants had only been performed on blood-related types of cancer, not what they call solid cancers, which refers to organ-related cancers.

Roughly speaking, the medical world differentiates between two types of cancer families. The first one includes cancers that attack the blood—hematological cancers. The second family includes cancers that attack one of the body's organs, such as prostate, breast, kidney, etc. These are called solid cancers.

Dr. S told us that in the United States, a kidney cancer patient underwent a bone marrow transplant and it was a success. He further explained that success rates are generally low, something like 20 percent. Perhaps in my case, he said, because my physical state and basic stats were fairly good, my chances of recovery were higher. Practically put, he said there was an option of transplanting bone marrow in a technique called mini-transplant stem cells, which required a bone marrow donor. The highest chance of finding a matching donor was among my siblings. He also spoke of the high cost of the transplant, insinuating that if it got to the point of execution, he could possibly perform it at a considerable discount if he could get money from a certain fund.

We came out of the meeting a little confused. Dr. S is an impressive, charismatic man who earns your trust. The idea of getting rid of this scum once and for all appealed to me, but the low success rates and the lack of track record in treating prostate cancer spoiled my hopes.

A mini-transplant of stem cells is a technique of transplanting bone marrow in three main stages. The first stage is finding a donor. A matching donor is a person who has undergone a tissue typing test and is found to match the patient's tissue type. The chance of finding matching tissues with a first degree relative is the highest. With siblings, for example, the matching probability is 25 percent.

After a donor is found, the patient receives a massive dose of chemotherapy. This treatment is aimed at destroying all the cancerous cells in the patient's body, as well as fully neutralizing his immune system. Neutralizing the patient's immune system is irreversible; therefore, risk to his life is great.

The third stage is transplanting the donor's bone marrow, which serves to rebuild the patient's immune system instead of his original one, enabling the body to better fight the cancerous cells that may still be nesting in his body despite the massive chemotherapy he has undergone.

We decided to move forward in two parallel directions—looking deeper into the matter and performing a tissue typing test for myself and my two siblings, to find out if one of the two was even a potential bone marrow donor for me.

My two brothers were willing to go to great lengths for me, so it was only obvious for them to take the tissue test and even donate bone marrow if need be. We did not know how this complex issue would develop, but it was a crucial step on the journey.

We made an appointment to consult Professor R, head of the hematological institute. He explained the main points to us once more. Unlike Dr. S, he believed that the mini-transplant stem cells technique sounded sexy, but was not at all applicable in my case. It involved many risks.

There are two cases in which the donor's bone marrow transplant is rejected by the patient's body. The first one is when the patient's immune system rejects the donor's transplant. This is called hostversus-graft (HVG). For this reason, the patient's immune system must be entirely neutralized using massive chemotherapy before the transplant is performed. The second case is when the transplant attacks the patient's body. This is called graft-versus-host disease (GvHD).

Perhaps in order to remain somewhat positive, he suggested I look into the option of joining a trial in the United States. He had no further details to provide, so this option remained mainly theoretical.

I researched the topic online and forwarded a question to the patients' forum—a source of information that never failed. Someone emailed me an article that was published in the *Daily Mail* on June 2002, about a metastasized prostate cancer patient on his deathbed, who had undergone bone marrow transplant. His body responded well to the treatment and fifteen months later, he was doing great. The transplant was performed by Dr. UlfHenrik Mellqvist from Göteborg University in Sweden. His work was also published in the British Journal of Hematology. I thought it important to notify Dr. S of this case so I emailed him the article.

We took a tissue typing test at the tissue typing unit in the Jerusalem hospital. It was nice to feel my brothers' strong desire to help me as best they could. Their unwavering support on all matters related to my condition gave me inner strength.

The tests were naturally not free and cost about a $1,000. I insisted on paying for the tests myself, although my brothers wanted to split the cost with me. Dr. S's office was nearby. I thought it would be a good idea to meet with him again. He made himself available and clarified that the decision was in our hands. If we, or rather I, wanted to go ahead with the transplant, he would do it. He shared with us the exciting news about a Swedish doctor who performed a transplant on a prostate cancer patient with success above and beyond the expected. I told him it was me who sent him the information. He was a little surprised, but ignored it elegantly. At the end of the meeting, he offered to reduce the cost of the procedure significantly. We decided that the reduced cost was no longer an obstacle if we chose to go ahead with the procedure.

Meanwhile, the test results came in and added more uncertainties. According to the tissue typing, Izhar- my younger brother was a full match as a donor, whereas my oldest brother, Arieh, was not. This would have been simple, had Izhar not been diagnosed with prostate cancer himself. The immediate question was if he would be able to serve as my donor at all. Was there a risk that his bone marrow might still be infested with prostate cancer cells, so that a transplant of his bone marrow into my body would cause unforeseen damage?

I spoke about it to Avivit, my ultimate consultant. In her flowery language, she claimed that Dr. S was willing to transplant anything in any body. She was not in favor of a transplant. There was nothing substantial in it for me, and the risks were great.

We scheduled another meeting, this time with Dr. Oren, Dr. S's deputy, in the same Jerusalem hospital unit. We told him about the tissue typing test results that showed Izhar as a full match. We also raised the issue of my brother's illness and its effect on the process. He did not have a clear answer to the latter; I guess he never faced such a situation before. Suddenly, his eyes sparked. He asked if the prostate gland removed from Izhar's body was kept frozen. Izhar said that to the best of his knowledge it was not. "Too bad," he said. "I could have done something with it."We did not investigate what exactly, but later, we extrapolated that he might have wanted to grind it and make some miraculous potion out of the gland that would cure anyone who drank it.

Dr. Oren is the total opposite of his boss. His office is tiny and crowded and he is a pleasant, straightforward man. There is no sign of Dr. S's extroverted manner. In his clear and simple words, he relieved us of our contemplations. He told us that the treatment was not suitable for a patient in my condition. It was very harsh and carried great risk. Therefore, it was only performed in cases where no other options were available, since the dilemma was between a certain death by the disease without a transplant, or a transplant whose recovery chances were slim. Since this was not my case, there was no room for this treatment. We left his office with a great sense of relief. It is amazing how a few clear and simple words can relieve the burden off a person's back—in my case, a life-altering decision.

We stepped out of the hospital into the warm Jerusalem summer breeze. It was evening by then. A feeling of lightness filled us. We went to a coffee shop to celebrate the important decision of not going forward with a bone marrow transplant.

CHAPTER THIRTEEN

I AM TWO YEARS OLD

November to December 2003

Yesterday, I turned fifty-two. It happens every year on November 23. This time, my birthday had a lot more meaning for me, since it was two years since I had been diagnosed with cancer. (I was diagnosed on October 28, to be exact.) According to the most optimistic forecast of my lifespan, I was supposed to be dead by now. Instead, I was still here, alive and kicking. Alive, for sure. Kicking? Only metaphorically, of course.

On Friday night, Rivka and Dina threw me a mini-surprise. We met my cousin, Amram, his wife Gila, Arieh, and Dina at a restaurant. The place was designed as a Wild West ranch with great solid wood ornamentation. We ordered wine. Arieh spoke about how he really got to know me and some of my qualities since I got sick. I was very touched and said that my inner strength came from my family's support, and that I could not have battled this scum without them. Rivka read a dedication she wrote for me. The essence of it was that I run two parallel timelines—the ordinary one from the day I was born and the other, from the day I was diagnosed. She congratulated me and mentioned how even the cellular company sent me a birthday message. (Before my birthday, I entered a reminder on my cell phone. We both happened to be sitting next to the computer when my cell phone flashed next to Rivka this message: "Happy Birthday. May you live till 75." I wrote "till 75" because it expressed my wish not to die too old, a wish I have had since the days when I was healthy. Rivka wondered how the cellular company knew it was my birthday. "What do you mean?" I said.
"They have my birth date.")

She finished her dedication with the words, "with love, Rivka'le," which I had not heard a lot those days. I was very touched and planted a wet one on her cheek. After that, I revealed that I was the one who congratulated myself, not the cellular company, and everyone laughed cheerfully.

I took the opportunity to wonder out loud about the topic of happiness. I said that some people had it all—money, a good family, a successful career, etc.—but were not happy because something was missing. Then there were the poor ones, who were happy with their lot, whereas even in my shitty condition, I had moments of happiness like all other people and perhaps even more, because I had the "privilege" to cherish and enjoy each day and sometimes each hour in which I lived without pain or suffering. Amram commented that religious people knew how to be happy with what they have because they felt grateful for it.

— ◊ —

Four months had passed since I stopped the chemotherapy. I really hope the disease is not quietly spreading inside my body. Every so often, I am "reminded" of it in the form of little aches and pains in different places in my body, and as always, with them arouse my fear that some new scum might be lurking, though none of my latest tests have shown any such thing. I had a major headache for a few days on one side of my head along with some blurry vision. After consulting Avivit and with Dr. Bassam's consent, I did a head and brain CT, but to our great relief, everything came out normal. I guess it is impossible to separate real physical sensations from those fueled by anxiety and fear.

All in all, I feel pretty good. True, I cannot exert any great physical effort, and I get tired quickly on long walks, but lately, all kinds of abnormal phenomena that have been bugging me, like tingling or fluttering inside my body, the "birds in the puddle" effect from the chemo, that was driving me crazy, seems to be slowly subsiding. I could say that unlike before, when I was three-quarters dead, today I am three-quarters alive. One of the annoying side effects that still bothers me is a kind of shortness of breath that comes on especially in the morning and with any effort I make.

I developed my own, private type of therapy—heat therapy. I learned that cancer cells are more sensitive to heat than healthy cells; therefore, if you expose them to high heat still bearable by health cells, there is a chance that they will die. There is actually a form of therapy called hyperthermia, in which a patient's body is exposed to a temperature of about 42°C (108°F). Along with radiation or chemotherapy, this yields better results than radiation alone. I decided to develop my own secret, "sophisticated" heat therapy of which I am the only patient. The only thing I can disclose here is that I bought a secret hairdryer I use daily to heat the areas with metastases. I do not know if it actually helps, and it may be risky, but the fact that I feel better than before encourages me greatly.

— ◊ —

Heating aside, I learned that blood clots are a life risk to every cancer patient with metastases. Some deaths among these patients are caused by blood clots that are carried into the heart, lungs, or brain. These clots are mainly formed in the leg veins and are called deep veinthrombosis (DVT). To reduce the risk, I take a blood-thinning drug. I have to ensure the exact dose, because if blood gets too thin, there is a risk of internal bleeding, which poses a life threat. But if the blood gets too thick, there is a risk of blood clots. The test for measuring the thickness of the blood is called international normalized ratio (INR), and the dosage must be suited to the test results. At some point, I was taking two pills a day and my INR test showed that my blood was thinner than normal. I immediately lowered the dose to one pill a day. Now the INR is a little low, so I increased the dose to one and a half pills a day. What is amazing to me is that my oncologist, Dr. Bassam, advised me not to use the drug for fear of bleeding. Doesn't he care about the real danger of blood clots I and other patients face? Am I wrong, or does this whole aspect go untreated among us patients? I know that there are other oncologists who do not use blood thinners with their patients. To my understanding, the reason is that the medical establishment believes it to be too complex for the patient to have to deal with. I wonder how many patients die due to blood clot complications.

— ◊ —

Yesterday, I took my routine blood tests. I try to take them every month to ensure that there is no unwanted development. The truth is that I am a unique patient, and it seems that my body responds differently to drugs than most people. The main and simple value for measuring prostate cancer is the PSA, of course. When it is low, it's a good sign, and when it is high, it's bad, but most important is its trend. That is, if the PSA is on a slope downward, the disease is in remission, and vice versa. At the time of my diagnosis, my PSA was over 560. After the chemo, it dropped to zero and stayed that way for a year and a half. It cannot go any lower than zero. It's truly fantastic. But, is my disease behaving accordingly? The doctors are in disagreement about what the PSA means. Avivit is consistent in believing that it reflects the true state of the disease, but says that at some point, the PSA will begin to rise and I will have to resume chemotherapy. Unlike her, Dr. Bassam and Dr. Ruby say that the PSA is no longer an indication of my disease. Either way, all three believe that there is no need for further treatment so long as I feel good.

Other blood test values that indicate the state of my disease come back normal;for instance, my alkaline phosphatase, which indicates the degree of activity in the bones. When it is high, it may indicate an abnormal activity in the bones, such as new metastases. But this value also came in low, luckily. However, according to the latest CT, there is some progression of the metastases in the spine. I hope this does not indicate that the disease is spreading, though I think I can feel the metastases in that area. Another bone scan shows various changes, some good and some bad. After weighing all the latest developments, the doctor wrote in his examination summary that there is a certain improvement. CT imaging can be done once a year. Bone scan may be done once every six months, no less. During the time in between, I have no reliable information about what is going on inside my body.

New research shows that too many CT tests increase the risk of getting cancer, due to the intense radiation the body is exposed to during the tests. Meaning that another type of cancer may develop in a patient who undergoes many CT scans. I take this point to heart and decide not to undergo any further CT tests unless I have a very good reason for them.

Tomorrow I am supposed to receive another Zoladex shot. As mentioned, this shot causes all kinds of nasty phenomena in the body, but first and foremost, it messes with the sexual drive.

One can stop taking the shot for a while, but that can sometimes cause severe or irreversible damage to the patient. On the other hand, taking a break can improve his quality of life immensely. Either way, it must be done under tight medical guidance and by an open-minded doctor. I heard about it from Dr. Tuck, the American doctor who consulted me. I stopped the treatment, but started feeling bad immediately. Perhaps it was my fear of stopping the treatment that was causing that. Anyway, I resumed my treatment, remembering that Avivit had warned me before that it was very dangerous and could cause paralysis or death. However, in our last meeting a few weeks ago, she raised this issue again. We did not exhaust the topic and I recently emailed her to ask if she would manage this topic for me. She has yet to respond. I needed to call her and find out her position.

I received my monthly test results I took two days ago. Not bad; not bad at all. My PSA continued to be zero, which was as good as it gets. All other values were faring positively. I also had Zomera treatment administered through the port installed in my chest. A routine matter of two hours in the oncology ward in Nahariya hospital.

At the end of the treatment, I returned to the nurses' station, booked my next treatment, and then bid them farewell. On the way out, I passed by the reception and asked Batya, the devoted secretary of the ward, to validate my parking slip.

I was lucky. My business, Teva Ez dairy in Ben-Ami village, was located on the other side of the street. I got into the car and was at the dairy in a matter of minutes. On treatment days, I tried not to run around too much and even go home early. It did not always work. On the days when I stayed late at the dairy, I was guilt-ridden and promised myself to go home early on the next treatment day. Most times, it did not happen.

CHAPTER FOURTEEN

TREATMENT AT ST. GEORGE CLINIC

Germany, April to May 2004

After much debate, research, and questioning, I decided to travel to Germany to undergo treatment at St.George hospital in the town of Bad-Aibling, about an hour's drive from Munich. The main treatment offered to me here was called whole body hyperthermia. The very decision to seek treatment there uplifted my spirits. I felt like I was once again in control of my life.

The policy I have adopted as a prostate cancer patient is not to wait for my condition to deteriorate, but to think a few steps ahead of the game, so I am always on watch for the scum. I know that if the scum jumps ahead of me, it will be hard to restore my condition.

According to the medical establishment, I required no further treatment at this stage, but I decided that I wanted this treatment. Naturally, there was a price to pay. Treatments don't last forever. Most of them cease to be effective after a while. The threat of having no treatment options left cast a dark shadow on me.

I clearly remember the moment I decided to come here. I was inspired by Shoval, one of the *Flotilla 13* fighters of the Israeli Navy Seals, who was diagnosed with cancer and succeeded in getting the Israeli Security Forces to acknowledge flotilla fighters as IDF-disabled veterans. Shoval told me he had two types of metastasized cancers in his internal organs and had undergone all possible chemo treatments in Israel, and had doctors remove whatever abdominal organs they could. He then traveled to Memorial Sloan Kettering Hospital in New York, which is the highest-ranked cancer treatment center in the world. He was joined by Josef, a high-ranking Shin-Bet[11] officer, who also had abdominal cancer. They were both offered additional chemotherapy. Shoval decided he could not take any more chemo and returned to Israel. Josef accepted their suggestion and continued to take chemo, but passed away shortly thereafter. Shoval had heard and researched about the St. George clinic, asking the army to fund his trip so he could be treated there. The army's medical division decided to first visit the clinic and check its treatment methods. After that, they agreed to fund the trip. Shoval told me that he was a healthy man today thanks to those treatments (my wishful thinking).

Rivka and I flew to Munich, where we were met by a driver who took us to the clinic. The place looked like a four-star hotel, only the guests here were cancer patients, some very ill. Most of them were accompanied by family members. Rivka's unyielding devotion proved itself especially in the most critical moments. She put on her angel wings and got down to work in her typical energized manner reserved for times like these.

One of the most important matters to handle when coming into the clinic was making sure the treatments were set forth right away so as not to waste time or miss them. We were told to watch out for this from patients who were previously treated here. Upon our arrival, and after much inquiry, I was taken for a physical examination that included an abdominal sonogram, executed by Dr. Gesner, a nice lady who felt me up quite thoroughly. I cannot deny that I was somewhat aroused by her touch. Apparently, a sonogram can be an enjoyable experience sometimes. She also told me she had visited Israel four years ago for three days.

During the examination, we chatted about cancer, as well as personal matters. But when the exam ended, so did the amicable attitude.

I had the impression that the medical team was not allowed to develop any friendly relationships with patients. Despite a few exceptions, as soon as the treatment ended, the relationship was over. I think it is proper and healthy, so as not to become too emotionally involved.

The treatment at the clinic was no small matter financially. The cost of three rounds, three weeks each, as the Germans suggested, was nearly $150,000. And I could need four rounds. Along with the flights and other expenses, we needed between $170,000 and $215,000.

Irit told us that her friends had organized a fundraising campaign for a woman named Nira who was sick with aggressive cancer. The clinic was the only option for saving her life. Due to all kinds of complications, she never received the treatment and passed away.

Taking Irit's lead, I decided to launch a campaign to raise the necessary funds. This is no simple decision. I, the "great" Itzy (well, only "financially" speaking), who was always well off and never needed to ask for money from family or friends, was going to launch a public campaign to raise money for my own sake. This required personal exposure, down to my underwear, and would obviously reflect on the kids and the extended family. In short, not a small matter.

I consulted Rivka about who would be the right person to run this project. I thought of Ilana, our good friend. Rivka suggested we take the management of the project on ourselves. She didn't want Ilana to get involved in our affairs. I consulted Irit and Izhar. Irit thought that we should not even consider managing it ourselves. "You have enough matters to handle and focus on," she said. In retrospect, I know she was right. When I spoke to Izhar, I sensed that he wanted to run the project, but I felt it would not be a good idea, since he lived far away and was very busy. He may not have had the time and energy required to invest in it.

Izhar said we needed someone to make the strategic decisions on the campaign. "What do you mean?" I said. "I will decide. I am the interested party and I will determine the campaign's strategic steps." I felt he was a little hurt by it, as if I was not giving him "a job." In hindsight, Izhar and Irit's contribution to the campaign was so significant that I doubt we could have launched such a complex effort without them.

I offered the job to Ilana, our neighbor and friend. She had experience in organizing events, and is energetic, meticulous, and quick. A real turbo engine. Ilana hesitated a little. She was very busy to begin with. She had a few questions, such as how much time it would require of her, etc. I told her that managing the campaign would require part-time work for about three months. As far as salary, I promised her we would work it out. I also made it clear that I would cover the campaign expenses.

This was the beginning of April. Ilana got down to work with her usual gusto. We received a lot of help from Irit and Izhar. They gave us all the material they had from Nira's campaign and hooked us up with Ofra Elkobi, chairman of the Struggle for Life organization. We set up a meeting with Nitzan, the guy who ran Nira's campaign, and some other entities in Jerusalem.

Nitzan gave us a lot of information about how to run the campaign, such as managing bank funds and many other technical details. He explained that we would need a CPA to oversee the finances, as well as an accountant to manage the flow of funds. He highly recommended we run the finances like a business in terms of accounting. During the meeting, we came up with ideas for how to promote the fundraising activities.

The social gathering was also successful. Our cousins arrived at Izhar's house later that morning, and my brother prepared a well-seasoned hummus, served with fresh pita bread and wine. We sat on his terrace, eating, drinking, and chatting. Izhar photographed me and then we inserted the best photo into the fundraising pledge page I had prepared in advance, according to the sample that was created for the late Nira, of blessed memory.

We felt good on the way home. The campaign was starting to become real. I also had an idea to produce a fundraising event for the local dairy owners at Teva Ez. Ilana liked the idea and began to work on the details. She wrote down who to invite in her notebook, so that by the time we got home, we had a guest list and a program all planned out.

Today I began my treatments at the St. George clinic. In the morning, I had my blood drawn, just like in Israel. Then Dr. Kroiff, whose unique feature is thick eyebrows, visited. He interviewed me to learn more about my condition. I showed him the bone scan and the test results from Israel. According to the results, he said I may be healthy after all...an interesting approach, which I had heard from a few doctors after meeting me for a second. There were two cancer markers that were perfectly balanced in my body—the first one was the PSA, which was zero, and the second one was the alkaline phosphatase, which is a parameter that indicates overactivity in the bones or the liver, and was showing a healthy person's result. However, the bone scan clearly showed the metastases. The doctor also mentioned that when there are bone metastases but the cancer disappears for some reason, it takes the bones a very long time to mend due to their slow pace of recovery, and this may be reflected in the images.

Later, a delegation of three doctors arrived in my room: Dr. Douwes, who was the top-ranking doctor in the clinic and the decision-maker, the nice female doctor, and Dr. Kroiff with the thick eyebrows. I was glad to see them, as I knew it was no small matter to have all three doctors visit a patient on his first day at the clinic.

The doctors asked me all kinds of questions about my cancer. They already obtained my medical file, which I had sent them when I first got in touch with the clinic. They consulted each other in German, and the nice female doctor explained that they are a bit hesitant about my diagnosis. My PSA and alkaline phosphatase did not indicate behavior typical of prostate cancer. Even the absorptions in my lungs were not typical of prostate cancer. Oops! That was getting interesting. In fact, a suspicion had arisen in the past as to my having cancer. The urologist that examined me twice in the last two years said I may not be sick at all, because he did not feel anything in my prostate after performing the invasive finger test.

At the end of the meeting, the doctors asked to see the prostate biopsy slides taken two and a half years earlier. We left them at home, so we had to call our son Orr and have him send them as soon as possible. I calculated the days and figured the slides would not be sent until the following day, because today was the eve of Independence Day and the post office would not be open tomorrow. Later on, I found out that the doctors postponed the main treatment I was supposed to receive (whole body hyperthermia) until the slides arrived. So, strangely enough, the Israeli Independence Day coincided with determining my treatment start date.

I wrote an email to Lenny, telling him among other things, how lucky I was because my life is always interesting. Indeed, I felt a constant movement inside me. Not all of it was positive, but there was no dull moment or boring routine.

We went to have dinner. Eating was the most common activity around here. The food was very diverse, plenty of vegetables, natural juices, and more. There were also different types of meat—most importantly lean, which suited us. Too bad we were eating too much.

Most of the patients in the clinic were American, Arab, or Israeli with their escorts. We befriended a Polish-American couple. The man was my age and had prostate cancer without metastases. He was diagnosed four years ago, and chose to go through orchiectomy[12] instead of undergoing a hormonal treatment.

The purpose of undergoing orchiectomy is to stop the production of testosterone among metastasized prostate cancer patients. This method was used in the past, before drugs like Zoladex were invented, which chemically stop the production of testosterone. This procedure is still used in extreme cases. Two noteworthy points in this technique are: One, the procedure is naturally irreversible, and two, there are psychological effects due to the certain feeling of "defect" it leaves the patient in an intimate level.

The "Poles" invited us on a drive to the Alps, which were very close to us. We drove out in their car just before sundown. We traveled through picturesque villages, saw a herd of buffalos grazing in the meadow, watched deer jumping about, and inhaled crisp mountainous air, so different than the air inside the stuffy clinic. We spoke a little about family and kids. He told us they had four adult children and could not have any more due to the surgery he had undergone. I told them that at our age, we needed grandchildren, and we no longer needed our testicles in order to have them. I was proud of myself, and they liked what I said and we all burst out laughing. Laughter no doubt uplifts both body and soul.

When we reached one of the German Alps, we stopped and walked around in the forest. It seemed to remind them of their home. Casey, the man, told us that they were busy building a house in the mountains of Connecticut. Their children had all left home and they did not need such a big place all to themselves. The house they were in the process of building was about 2,370 square feet, which they considered small.He also said that they drilled a well about 400 feet deep in order to have water supply. They used an "expert" service to determine where to drill. The expert's method was simple: He held a branch horizontally in his hand and walked around until he saw the branch bend, then ordered the drilling to be done at that spot. When I asked him why the branch bent, he explained that it is due to some magnetic field created by an area with water. By the way, Casey was an electrical engineer with a senior position in a regional electric company in the United States, so I was rather surprised by these strange techniques he was swearing by. I told him I just had an electromagnetic treatment today but nothing bent with me. He laughed and said that in my case, everything bent needed to straighten. We shared some more hearty laughter, then climbed into the car and began to make our way back to the "institution."

— ◊ —

Today I received two treatments. One was a one-hour external hyperthermia to my chest, using radio waves in the area where the metastases developed. I did not feel much sensation, but it was done on a water bed and was truly hypnotizing, so much so that I fell asleep and my soul drifted, almost uncontrollably, into the infinite universe.

The second treatment, given here on a daily basis, was electromagnetic therapy. The patient lays on a bed, and a magnetic field of 25 megahertz (25 million pulses a second) was applied to me for ten minutes.

This magnetic field is supposed to kill cancer cells. The technical logic behind it is as follows: Every object in nature has resonance. The simplest example for it is a swing. The number of cycles a swing makes in a certain time unit is fixed, regardless of the height it reaches. The number of cycles it does in one second is called its "resonance". If you push it very lightly with the same resonance rate—that is, if every time, when the swing reaches its maximum height, you push it toward the direction of its movement—it will swing higher. It will keep reaching higher with each additional push, until something interrupts its movement. This is what they are trying to do to the cancer cells using magnetic energy. They cause them to swing on and on in their resonance until they are destroyed.

In any case, this treatment made me feel somewhat better with my pelvic metastases. *Was it really working? Who could tell? I hoped so.*

— ◊ —

Since the biopsy slides did not arrive yet, my whole body hyperthermia treatment was postponed once more. The nurse in charge notified me of it when I happened to pass by the office in the afternoon. There was some chaos in the German order here. After all, there is a whole series of preparations that must happen before this treatment: The day before, one must eat a light breakfast, then take in only fluids, and begin fasting from six in the evening. One must also do an enema to clean out one's guts, because the procedure must be performed on an empty stomach. They also do an echocardiogram, to check the lung functioning, and stop any ongoing treatments.

I was already in the midst of preparations when she notified me that the treatment was postponed because they were waiting on the slides.

With that, I rushed to the local hyperthermia station and explained to Nurse Sabina that the treatment was postponed. I asked her to use the time to receive this other treatment instead. She admitted me immediately, lay me on the water bed, and caressed my face in her own special way before turning on the appliance that heated my internal organs. Sabina is an older, good-looking woman with Cleopatra-style bangs. She likes to hug and kiss her patients whenever she can, and so she does with me. This local hyperthermia is very soothing. I fell into deep sleep within minutes. The bell on the device rang about an hour later, announcing that the "trip"was over. She usually gave me time to recover, but today she had another patient in line, so she was impatient as she rushed me to get dressed. Still sleepy, I got dressed and walked out to recuperate in the reception area.

The biopsy slides finally arrived. Rivka approached me with the parcel our son, Orr, had sent us. I was excited, as we were about to solve the riddle: Did I have prostate cancer or some other scum? We found Dr. Kroiff (with the thick eyebrows) and gave him the parcel. He opened it ceremoniously and immediately called the lab in Rosenheim, the town district about twenty minutes away, requesting a re examination of the slides. Tomorrow is May 1 —a holiday here—and the following day is Sunday, another day off. In short, I did not expect to receive the results before Monday.

— ◊ —

The fund raising campaign and going abroad were very important events for me, both practically and from an emotional–social standpoint.

On the practical side, we had to handle many technical details. Even before we met in Jerusalem, we invited our extended family to a work meeting at our house. That included Arieh, Dina, Izhar, and Irit, as well as Rivka's siblings, their spouses, and her parents. I asked the dairy's CPA to oversee the financial aspect. He volunteered to do it. The ongoing accounting was entrusted to Yossi, the dairy's bookkeeper. He also did it on a voluntary basis. I made sure they met with Ilana to coordinate the work method.

In the family meeting, Ilana explained to everyone that our goal was to raise money to fund my treatments. The main idea was that each one of them would be a hub that would open more hubs, with each hub engaged in raising funds for my complex project. Arieh, my brother did not like the idea of asking people for donations in the manner we presented. In my previous conversations with him, he had offered to raise all the funding needed from the family. He felt that asking for donations was like begging and not becoming to our family. I told him very clearly that I was not willing to compromise his family's fortune for my illness, and that I refused to accept their private funds to pay for my treatments overseas. I told him that nobody knew how much money would be needed for my sake and that I had no right to use their savings and lead them to impoverishment due to my illness.

Yoav, my nephew, also got carried away in wanting to invest his savings in me. He sat next to me, embracing me and saying he would open up his savings account to contribute to the campaign. It moved me to tears, but I explained to him that this was not my intention. I told him that opening his savings was unnecessary, and that the idea was to raise small amounts from many sources so that no one ended up poor. To validate this point, I spoke to Dina and asked her to make it clear that I objected to any family funding. I hoped my messages came across.

Arieh said that begging door-to-door was not for him. But Later he came up with a great idea later on. He suggested producing an event in the lot behind his house, where Yoav got married, and charging a cover fee that would go toward the campaign. Everyone liked the idea and Arieh felt more comfortable this way.

Ilana made a contact list of names, addresses, emails, and phone numbers for key team members.

At the end of the meeting, we gave each participant a preliminary pledge sheet. We asked everyone not to distribute them until we completed a final draft.

Ilana took the pledge sheet to Tami, a graphic designer in our village, who did the graphic layout. Ilana and I disagreed about the design of the pledge page. She wanted the page to include her introduction and to be emailed, or handed, with her words included. I insisted that the pledge be an attachment to an email, so that each one of our team members could send it to different people, adding their own introductory words when relevant, and keep the pledge page unanimous and unchanged. I knew it should be this way, even though Ilana disagreed. I made it gently clear that I was the one to decide on this matter. And I did. Ilana distributed the pledge letter to her mailing list and so did I. The pledge was on its way.

Two days later, Izhar called me to say that we should add a comment to the pledge that would clarify that the donations were tax deductible. This was after I had deliberately omitted this comment from the sheet, thinking it was obvious and gave a too much of a business feel to the pledge instead of the sublime message I was trying to get across. After some debate, we added it to the pledge and issued a second draft.

A few days later, Izhar called again to tell me he knew a news anchor at TV Channel 1. She read the pledge and thought it was not strong enough. She said it was too cold and lacked emotion, thus would not yield the anticipated donations. She wrote an alternative pledge that was indeed more emotional, but also too revealing with some facts exaggerated. For instance, she wrote that the "doctors could not believe how much better my condition got." I thought her draft was good, but I changed whatever felt too personal and overrated regarding my medical condition. Instead of writing that "the metastases had spread all over my body by the time I was diagnosed," I wrote, "the disease was progressive by the time it was diagnosed." I did not want the entire world to be privy to all my medical details, nor did I think it would help to raise money. With Tami's help, Ilana issued a third draft of the pledge, which we distributed to all our friends.

No medical treatments were administered at the clinic during weekends. It allowed time for the patients and their escorts to rest and freshen up. The clinic staff was also in charge of weekend activities. One activity scheduled for today, Saturday, was a trip to Chiemsee Lake, about an hour and a half away. We heard it was a nice lake with two islands in the middle and a monastery on each—one for monks (the larger island, of course) and one for nuns. The monks' island also housed the castle of King Ludwig II (of whom I knew nothing). The trip was supposed to commence at noon from the plaza near the clinic. We ate a quick lunch and walked to the plaza. A few more patients were waiting there, but the bus never arrived. Apparently, the trip was cancelled for some reason and we were never notified. So we took a walk around the lovely town center and returned to the clinic.

A new problem I have encountered in the last few months is the increasing swelling of my legs. Being swollen, they hurt even after a short walk. I spoke to Dr. Gasnier about it and she promised to see to it that I got the proper treatment. So far, nothing has happened.

In the evening, I went online and wrote to the Germans who hosted my nephew, Yoav, when he was here with the IDF-disabled delegation. We shall see what comes of it.

— ◊ —

Sunday. We woke up this morning to the sound of rain. A winter day. But there was no wind, and the rain was mild, unlike the whipping, lashing rain in Israel. It wasn't even that cold. Like yesterday, we had a free day, and the program included a day trip to Kitzbühel, a resort town in the Ausrian Alps.

We went down for breakfast. I must eat three meals a day here, because I have to take pills before and after each one.

The trip was a lot of fun. We crossed the border from Germany into Austria. The border posts are completely deserted and nobody stopped us for passport control. The landscape is breathtaking; everything is lush and green, surrounded by water...it doesn't get any better. Kitzbühel itself is a gorgeous ski resort town with many ski lifts. It also hosted a display of vintage cars from the Bavarian antique club. Such beautiful, shiny antiques that looked like they had just been taken off the production line.

— ◊ —

Back to the campaign. I felt compelled to describe it in detail, since this heartfelt project symbolizes the essence of goodness in human spirit. The very knowledge that close and distant people came together to support my cause and were working so hard for the success of this campaign to fund my treatment made it that much more moving.

Choosing Ilana as the campaign manager proved successful. She has the ability and charisma needed to raise such a project. She recruited volunteers from our village to help with printing, sending the pledges, making phone calls, and any other necessary activity. She established a village brainstorm committee, and they decided to hold a bazaar sale on the Shavuot Holiday, with all of its proceeds going toward my campaign. The big commotion around it made me feel slightly uncomfortable, but the end result is what counts. And indeed, the campaign began to bear fruit. The funds began to flow in—by check, cash, and verbal commitment, first from my village and then from wider circles. We received information about future donations coming our way from many different sources.

— ◊ —

Today, we received the results from the local lab. "Surprisingly" enough, the German lab results are identical to the ones from Israel, meaning, that I indeed have metastasized prostate cancer. The cost of the test and related expenses was over $400. Another Israeli couple arrived today—Sarit and Ofer. Sarit has liver cancer. She has already been treated in a U.S. clinic. They told us that the costs are much higher there and that St. George is a real "find" in comparison.

Tomorrow I am scheduled to undergo the first whole body hyperthermia treatment. It involves gradually heating up the body to nearly 42°C (close to 108°F). When the desired temperature is reached, the patient is given a low dose of chemo IV along with Glucose. Then the body is gradually cooled down.

The logic behind this treatment is that cancer cells weaken under heat. They also like glucose and feed on it. Once they are weakened by the heat, they are served the glucose along with the chemo, and "swallow" the glucose and chemo cocktail that kills them (so we hope.)

The entire process is highly monitored, checking the heart activity, respiration and other parameters, so that the patient is not under risk if something unexpected happens. The process lasts six hours under general anesthesia. The recovery time lasts a few hours after that. Some patients are only sent back to their rooms the following morning. The preparations include a thorough enema, which is highly unpleasant, but performed with the most advanced technology.

Alfonso, the Austrian who did my enema, boasted about having given enema about 12,000 times. After inserting the end of the flexible instrument into my anus, he began to pump a special solution into my guts. A few seconds later, I began to feel all kinds of developments in my stomach, and the "product" was sucked out through a clear tube. Each time it came out, I grunted as one does when constipated, and Alfonso grunted in satisfaction with his professional expertise, calling out, "Gutte, gutte," in a typical German accent. He reported the quantity and speed of the enema contents to me. Every so often, he lifted the tube, inviting me to see the contents flowing out. Toward the end, the machine pushed pure oxygen to disinfect the intestines from inside, which made me feel as if someone just released a soda "balloon" into my stomach. In short, it was far from enjoyable. Even a few hours after the procedure, my guts were still engaged in some unpleasant internal activity—apparently due to the "soda." Following the procedure, I had to fast, too. I just hoped all this suffering was not in vain.

Tomorrow, while I undergo hyperthermia, the Teva Ez dairy would host the fundraiser event. I spoke to Ilana, Izhar and Arieh, and it seemed like it is going to be a success. Izhar was preparing a video segment, Arieh was going to read something I wrote in his name, Lenny was going to talk about prostate cancer and Smadar, Illan's good friend and a village neighbor, would sing a song. I asked for it to be a song by Nathan Alterman,[13] whose songs I have loved for forty years, ever since I received his book of poems as a gift for my Bar Mitzvah. Thirty high-profile industrialists, manufacturers and local businessmen are scheduled to arrive. Writing about the activity taking place for my sake, gave me the chills. Too bad I could not watch it from here. I would probably still be coming off the anesthesia when the event took place. I asked Izhar and Irit to film it. It would be interesting to watch it when I got back.

On Tuesday, ten days after our arrival, I finally underwent a whole body hyperthermia. I thought it would be a piece of cake, but it wasn't, to say the least. After all the preparations, the day started with the male nurse telling me to lay naked on a heated bed with a heated canopy. He hooked me up to all kinds of gauges: an 8-inch long thermometer shoved up my anus to take my temperature—the second and probably not the last time they shove something up there. They had to ensure that my body temperature did not exceed 42°C (108°F), since in that heat, the proteins in the body change their composition irreversibly (or as Shimon Peres[14] once said: "You can make an omelet from an egg, but you can't make an egg from an omelet"). The nurse also hooked me up to an automatic blood pressure gauge on my arm, placed a clip on my finger to read my pulse, and finally placed electrodes on my chest to monitor heart activity.

After all these preparations, he ran a blood test, which was normal. Then they placed a mask over my face and ran the anesthetics into me.

From that moment on, I remembered nothing; my memory was simply blank. I do recall myself later in the process lying in bed and trying with all my might to get up, while under complete sedation. My devoted Rivka, who was by my side that whole night, said I went wild and kept trying to get out of bed. They tied me to the bed to prevent me from doing so, just like they do to lunatics in the movies, and then added more anesthetics.

They finally let me go back to my room. I couldn't walk by myself and my speech was garbled, like a drunkard slurring his words. I wanted to say something, but it came out unclear. In short, I was a mess. Today, about 30 hours later, I was starting to recover from treatment, though I still felt like I have a slight flu. And I was naïve enough to think it would be a walk in the park.

Rivka was supposed to fly back tomorrow, May 7. But after seeing me through the whole body hyperthermia, she said it is inhuman to let someone go through this treatment without someone at their side. She decided to stay another nine days, despite her desire to get back to the kids and her commitments for her master's program at the university. To be honest, after realizing how tough this treatment was, I was rather worried that she would not be there with me for the next round. I was happy she decided to stay.

$$- \Diamond -$$

I was feeling better. Aside from my swollen legs that kept bothering me, the unpleasant cancer-related sensations were nearly all gone, and touch wood— I seemed to be heading in a positive direction. I did not know if I could fully recover from the scum, but there was no doubt that my unique journey was bearing fruit.

We went down for breakfast. I had no choice but to eat three meals a day so I could take my pills on a full stomach. Like the others, I received a pillbox divided into four compartments filled with pills. One compartment had six pills to be taken half an hour before each meal, and the other three compartments had about ten pills each, to be taken during each of the three meals. Five more pills per meal were added two days prior to and three days following the whole body hyperthermia. In addition to the pills, I got three bags of IV each day. One had vitamin C, one had selenium, an antioxidant, and the third had a substance that reinforced the immune system. All of them were given in high concentrations. So if I took 200 micrograms of selenium per day in Israel, here I was given 1,500 micrograms three times a week. All in all, you could stuff yourself just on pills and IVs.

Despite general improvement, my swollen legs were getting worse. They hurt and made it difficult to walk even a short distance. I brought this to the doctors' attention, and they explained that my lymphatic system is not working efficiently enough to carry lymphatic fluids upward from the legs. They offered me a lymphatic drainage massage in my legs along with homeopathic drops three times a day. The massage was given by Alfonso, the enema and massage expert. What was nice about this place was that it offered a holistic treatment that yielded results. In the past, I had complained to Dr. Bassam about my legs swelling, but he just stared at me, frowning, never suggesting any solution.

The lymphatic system is more or less parallel to the circulatory system of the blood. It is a network of lymphatic vessels that carry lymphatic fluid from various body cells to the heart. Lymphatic fluid contains substances that are secreted from the cells. If this system malfunctions and the flow of the lymph is hindered, the fluid accumulates and causes the organ in which the flow is stagnated to swell.

The issue of lymphatic fluid flow in the legs is highly sensitive, since it has a long distance to cover on its way upward toward the heart, against gravity. This is why swollen legs are so common. The causes of that can be chemotherapy or damage to the lymph glands. Overweight people also suffer from this problem. Fat presses on lymph vessels and glands, interrupting proper function of the system. One of the most efficient treatments in this case is lymphatic drainage massage, which gently encourages lymphatic fluid to flow in the desired direction toward the heart.

I felt a strong urge to write more about how we were sent off to Germany, since it was a special, moving, and amazing process no superlative can describe. The day before we left, we received many phone calls and visits from family members, close friends, and those I did not even imagine would show up—such as one neighbor with whom my relationship had gone sour after fighting over her refusal to pick up her trash, which was scattered by dogs and cats on our lawn time and time again. This neighbor showed up to say goodbye to us, embraced me warmly, and began to weep on my shoulder, getting me all teary-eyed. Who would have thought?!

The campaign started to show results, and significant funds began to flow into the account—an anonymous envelope with $1,500 cash; a check for $1,500 from a neighbor who did not even have money to buy falafel (I really want to pay him back); and more. The neighbor explained that it was a donation made by his brother in the United States who had heard about me. Many such gestures touched me immensely. The event at the dairy went well and raised over $10,000. Ilana was no doubt an excellent producer, and the others did their share, too. It felt like one of those rare moments when an entire community enlists for a great cause, and that great cause was the "one and only" Itzy Be'er. But, on the flip side, it was the first time in my life that I received money from people. I felt uncomfortable with it. It created a certain emotional commitment to each one of my donors. From now on, my actions would be closely monitored, placed under a magnifying glass. I knew it would be hard for me when I return home, feeling like everyone was some sort of a partner to my treatments and finances. Let's say I decide to buy a new car or renovate the house. I would have to think twice. What are they going to say? "Why is he using our money for that?" As

they say: there are no free meals.

Yesterday, Markus and Verna Neuman and their four children came to visit us at the clinic. This family hosted my nephew, Yoav, at their home last year. They traveled more than five hours each way to visit us—an Israeli couple they did not even know. That was above and beyond the call of duty. They were nice people. Their kids brought us drawings, and the parents some candy, and we went on a trip to Chiemsee Lake not far from here. We had interesting conversations about all kinds of philosophical matters, including the Holocaust.

Tomorrow will be the second and last time for this round of whole body hyperthermia. Today was another day of intense preparations, culminating in a thorough enema by Alfonso the great.

It was almost ten at night, and I was alone in the room. Rivka went out with other Israelis. I was fasting ahead of my treatment. and there were more preparations to be made. I was glad that she went out. She usually enjoys this. Besides, she had a hard time with the fact that I had become the center of the family's attention ever since I got sick and she was pushed aside. I know it was tough for her. After all, she was cut off from her entire life back home to be by my side at the clinic. However, our relationship had reached a certain equilibrium, which made me feel like it was stable and stood the test.

I spoke to Yoav, Izhar, and Dina on the phone today. I got so much support from my family, it was unbelievable. I told Dina that I had the best family in the whole world. We were silent for a few good moments, taken by our emotions and unable to speak. Then she said that she felt a chill all over her body. An hour after I hung up, I was still moved to tears.

— ◊ —

Yesterday, I underwent a whole body hyperthermia for the second time. This time, the recovery was a little easier. I did not try to get out of bed or go wild that night, and I was more lucid and pretty much functional a few hours after the treatment ended.

We began to resolve our financial matters ahead of our departure on Sunday. Since the weekend started on Friday, we had to settle our payments by tomorrow. This was a basic, simple matter, but required many phone calls, faxes, etc. We also needed to stock up on medication for the remainder of our time back home. Rivka ran relentlessly, taking care of these matters.

Upon completing all of our errands, we were happily ready to return home.

---

11 Israeli Security Services.

12 A surgical procedure in which one or both testicles are removed.

13 An Israeli poet, playwright, journalist, and translator (1910–1970).

14 Former prime minister and ninth president of Israel.

15

16

CHAPTER FIFTEEN

A SECOND VISIT TO ST. GEORGE CLINIC

Germany, June to July 2004

My health issues seemed to keep me endlessly preoccupied. It started a few weeks before our second visit to the clinic. I found out that one of my liver values, called ALT (GPT), was abnormal. This had never happened before. The norm is up to 52 units per liter. My first blood test indicated 86, and the second test, four days later, reached 159—almost doubling itself. My blood counts were also low. It worried me, because such deviation may indicate metastases in the liver—something I would rather not think about. I called Ruthie and consulted Dr. Nabil, as well as Avivit. All of them tried to calm me down, explaining that an abnormal result due to metastases must reach a numerical value of a few thousands. My abnormal results may indicate some infection, virus, or the like. I was not thoroughly convinced, and with this uncertainty, we flew back to Germany.

It had been two months since my last visit to St. George clinic. In many ways, this visit felt entirely different than the first one.

For one thing, I was no longer worried about the unknown, as I had been on my first visit here. This time it was clear, familiar, and natural. Yoel, our good friend, and other village friends visited us the night before we left. We made a few phone calls to family and other friends, but it was more of a routine this time.

I had a realization in the last few weeks that my relatively good condition after the first visit was getting less so as time went by. Different sensations came back to bother me. It could be that I overexerted myself again. I was well aware that any physical exertion made me feel bad and was followed by tingling of sorts all over my body, which demoralized me. The thing is that I, Itzy Be'er, who come from a lineage of farmers, have spent all my life enjoying all kinds of activities that require physical effort. It was very hard for me to accept the simple fact that any physical attempt caused negative symptoms and that I was, in fact, physically limited. Despite being aware of my limitations, I kept testing and challenging myself with various activities, only to find out once more that they brought on pain or tingling that tipped me off balance.

In the short time period between my two visits to St. George clinic, I spent time at the dairy, but I felt a little out of place. My mind was elsewhere. But May is a good month for the dairy, ahead of the Shavuot Holiday, and it was especially busy this year. People bought cheese like crazy for the holiday, and this seasonal buzz gave me some respite from the madness in my own life.

We were about to fly to the clinic for our second visit. Last time, we hardly slept the night before leaving. Our flight was departing at three in the morning; therefore, we had to get to the airport around midnight, plus drive two and a half hours from Mitzpe Hila to the airport. Thus, we had another long, sleepless night ahead of us.

The flight to Munich was quite annoying, since the plane was at full capacity. I had a window seat, so I could hardly get up. My legs swelled up again due to the lengthy sitting. I was relieved when the flight was over.

Ofer and Sarit, whom we met on our first visit, were on the plane with us. Sarit, who has liver cancer, was in a pretty bad condition. Ofer rented a car at the Munich airport, and we drove together, for an hour, to the clinic. We arrived in the afternoon and met up with all the staff members we already knew. I met Sabina again, the nurse in charge of local hyperthermia, telling her that my Israeli friends were jealous because I had been kissed by a German nurse on my first treatment at the clinic. She laughed heartily and kissed me once more.

I took some more blood tests today. My liver values have improved considerably are within normal range now, except for one that was slightly off. The doctors here have also said that such deviation had no significance. On the other hand, my blood counts were still alarmingly low.

On my first visit, I paid around $2,700 to test my sensitivity to various chemo drugs. I asked about the test results and was told that I was partially sensitive to most chemo drugs available, which meant they would only be partially effective. But the damage caused to the body would be of course full. No breaks there. This may be because I have already used so many chemo drugs before.

They took another sonogram. It is not the most accurate exam but gives a pretty good picture of the abdomen. The worst finding was that I had a lot of gas in my stomach. Let it suffice. I told the doctor who performed the exam that I am a "walking gas station." She smiled her polite German smile. She is very tall and pretty but down to business. She is young enough to be my daughter, a nice German lady doctor.

We met Dr. Douwes, the head doctor, again today. Apparently, he was one of the clinic owners, so it was no small matter to sit him down to a conversation. We learned that the best way to achieve that was to leave a message that I wanted to meet with him with all the other staff on site. In the meeting, we discussed my low blood counts and the treatment results. When the blood count is too low and treatments are held off, this can have grave consequences on a cancer patient, including death. I expressed my concern in continuing the chemo, and he said they offered whole body hyperthermia without chemo, which strengthens the immune system and indirectly helps fight the cancer. He suggested we do two more treatments with chemotherapy and then do the treatments without chemo on my next visit. We got the impression that he opted for the chemo, but his German politeness made him offer a later treatment without chemo. We figured he knew what he was saying when advocating for chemo.

When I brought up my swollen legs, he explained once again that it had to do with the lymphatic system in my legs and advised me to continue lymphatic massage. He took this problem seriously and even did a sonogram to make sure nothing else was causing the swelling. Luckily, nothing suspicious was detected. The doctor himself was very fat, and he explained that, as a fat person, he suffered from the same problem because his big belly pressed on the lymph fluid pipe, interrupting the upward flow and causing his legs to swell while walking. I was "glad" to hear that, because I felt like he understood the problem firsthand. He suggested I wear elastic compression socks that compress the leg and thus prevent swelling. I explained to him that in the Israeli summer, there is no chance I would wear them. I decided to pursue lymphatic massage in Israel, as well.

We also discussed my abnormal liver values. He reassured me that my GGT—the value that indicates liver metastases—was within norm and I did not need to worry about it.

We left the meeting rather pleased, but I was still worried about my low blood count.

Today, Friday, I was prepped by Alfonso, the enema expert, for my whole body hyperthermia scheduled for Monday. Alfonso also said I had a lot of gas in my stomach. He cracked up when I told I was a "walking gas station."

Monday was not a good day to do whole body hyperthermia, because the preparation started on Friday. On Sunday afternoon, I would have to drink two liters of a disgusting laxative, since the treatment had to be done on an empty stomach. I also had to abstain from solid food and drink only liquids for a half a day before the treatment.

When we reached our room, we were touched to find a beautiful flower arrangement from Markus, our German friend. The man has a big heart, no doubt. I called him and thanked him sincerely.

Saturday. The clinic was slow during the weekend. We decided to leave for the weekend to change the scenery and save some money. The daily cost of accommodation at the clinic was about €870 ($900). One night at a good hotel was about $105, and saving our room at the clinic costs $80, so it saves us about $750 per day. Earning that much money per day is not bad. In fact, you can live off it while you go traveling. This can set you up for life.

Before we left, I met with Dr. Reich, who was in charge of the whole body hyperthermia treatment. I told him I was hesitant about undergoing the treatment on Monday.

Right away, he said, "No problem, we will cancel it."

"But", I said, "Wait a minute, I want your advice. Cancelling is easy." I explained to the doctor that my blood count was too low and that I was afraid that it would drop even more as a result of the treatment. Moreover, the benefit from the chemo would only be partial, as reflected in the test results from my first visit. Since my illness was in remission, there was no urgent need to undergo chemo. To our surprise, he adopted my approach at once and suggested hyperthermia without chemo, as Dr. Douwes suggested two days ago.

I asked him if this would be beneficial, and he said that the treatment has no direct effect on the cancer, but it strengthens the immune system and helps the body battle the cancer indirectly. He also said I had until Monday morning to decide on the type of treatment, since the preparations were the same.

Dr. Reich had a "movie actor" look, blond and tall. Two days before, he came to my room to sign me on a consent agreement to receive the treatment. Signing this agreement was like signing a mortgage contract—a thick document with endless clauses written in small English print that protects the clinic against any law suits.

When the doctor walked into my room, my laptop was playing Pink Floyd's *The Wall*. He asked if it was Pink Floyd, and I said yes. We started chatting. I told him my son asked us to buy him this CD in the airport on the way here. Then he asked me how old my son was and I told him he was a soldier in the army. We started talking about politics for a bit. He thought that the situation between the Palestinians and us was so complex that he no longer understood who was against who and why. I agreed, saying that even for us Israelis, it was sometimes hard to figure it out.

After much debate and consultation with Rivka, we decided to take the treatment with the chemo component. In retrospect, I find that this suits my **"way of the cat"** strategy in fighting the scum with many hard blows until it is destroyed.

Later on Saturday, we traveled to a mountainous region in the Austrian Alps called Kaisergebirge. It was about an hour away from the clinic, but felt like the end of the world. At some point, the road ended, leaving only dirt paths for hikers and all-terrain vehicles. There were also bustling hotels and shops for tourists. We walked around in this beautiful area with cliffs, leftover winter snow, forests, green all around, and cows peacefully grazing in the vast meadows. This time, we brought our digital camera, and I took many pictures. One of the hikers took a picture of Rivka and me. Rivka did not like to be photographed and got annoyed when I asked her permission to take her picture. I think photographs are meaningful, because as time goes by, they keep us "forever young."

We returned to the hotel near the clinic. Linder Romantic Hotel was indeed pristine, and the wing where we stayed had been recently remodeled, so everything looked new and shiny—the taps, towel hangers, and accessories were gold coated. The bed was made to the nines, with new, scented sheets. It was almost a pity to lie down and crease them. The dining hall had tables for two with potted plants that had red hearts threaded through them. A true romantic getaway. At night, we went into town and walked around. We found a nice restaurant and had dinner.

Changing ambience from the semi-depressing clinic to the fresh-air outdoors infused new strength in us.

— ◊ —

We returned to the clinic on Sunday afternoon to finish preparing for the wholebody hyperthermia treatment. The laxative gave me terrible diarrhea and nausea.

We decided to take a walk in area of the clinic, but I felt so bad that we came back a few minutes later. .

— ◊ —

I underwent the treatment yesterday and woke up this morning, twenty-four hours after it began, disoriented and confused. I feel extremely tired; so much so that even speaking was a difficult task and my speech comes out slurred, with lots of "hhaaa" and "bahhh." But I am slowly recovering. It is nighttime now, and I am well enough to write. Patients who are severely ill lie in bed for three days after the treatment, but in my case, people see me in the dining room a day after and commend me on my quick recovery.

— ◊ —

I am sitting in my room, hooked up to an 1.5-liter IV bag with a vitamin C concentrate, which works in some way to eliminate the cancer cells, and writing at the same time.

Yesterday, we took a long walk around the town and happened upon a shopping area outside the town center. After buying clothes and some other items, we began to walk back. The way back was pretty tough for me and we had to rest on a bench, like two elderlies. I was nauseous and did not feel like eating lunch. Further down the way, we saw a small grocery store. I fancied their watermelon cut into quarters. I had such a craving for it that I forgot I was nauseous. Back in the room, I devoured the fruit. It was not as tasty as Israeli watermelons, but it was a great buy and it refreshed me and allowed the nausea to pass. By dinner time, my appetite was back to normal.

Our German friend, Markus, offered to visit us this coming Saturday. I look forward to seeing him.

We learned about a beer and music festival taking place not far from the clinic. A few of us Israeli patients and escorts decided to go. According to the directions we got, it was supposed to be about twenty to thirty minutes away on foot. But once we started walking, we realized it was a lot longer. It was close to nine in the evening by then and nearly dark outside. Two youths we met on the way told us that we had another five kilometers to go. Our gang heard that and wanted to turn around. Although I was pretty tired, I convinced them and myself that it made more sense to keep walking the short distance left, enjoy ourselves, and take a taxi back. Our friends were not convinced and decided to go back to the clinic, but Rivka and I carried on. We reached the festival within minutes. There was a giant tent decorated with various beer manufacturers' ads and a brass band with singers playing music for a huge beer-drinking crowd. It was not terribly exciting, but I felt really good, because I managed to walk that long way without any problem, and because we insisted on making it instead of going back to the clinic. Whenever you give up on something, you feel like you are missing the real thing; I wanted to live a real life.

I want to express my gratitude to Rivka on this. She was willing to follow me on almost any adventure, with natural curiosity and courage that allowed us to achieve great things sometimes. I am also very appreciative of her patience and willingness to invest effort in me and sacrifice her many obligations—home, kids, work, studies, etc. In general, escorting a patient is rather frustrating for the caregiver, because he is virtually in service of the patient at any given moment. While a patient attracts everybody's attention, a caregiver is like a shadow whose effort earns no recognition for the most part.

Even though there was not much to do here and getting bored was pretty easy, Rivka had the ability to keep herself busy, whether through sightseeing, social activities, or reading.

Markus, our German friend, came to visit us at the clinic with three of his youngest children.

They were so pleasant and easygoing that one could not help but fall in love with them. The love they showered on us, the Israelis, was limitless and hard to put into words. I asked him why his family wanted to visit us, and he explained it was kind of a revelation (divine perhaps) that led him to become religious about twenty years ago. He said that a few years back, he and his family decided to dedicate all of their efforts to supporting Jews—and especially Israel and Israelis—and have been running projects to commemorate the Holocaust ever since. They recently marched in silence through the same route in which Jews in their town had been led to the train station during World War II. Now they were busy preparing an international Holocaust event to commemorate sixty years since the Nuremberg trials, to be held next year. At first, they wanted to hold it in Nuremberg itself, but due to foreseeable objections, it will be held elsewhere. His wife did not join him on this visit, since she was busy with secondhand sales to fund a project for Israel.

Markus invited us to visit them next weekend. In fact, he did not leave us any choice. We wanted to fly back to Israel on Sunday, but he insisted on our postponing our flight till Monday so he could drive us to the airport—a threehour ride. Rivka was not thrilled, but we decided to postpone the flight and stay with them until Monday morning.

In an idle moment, I showed Markus's kids a trick I know with a pencil. The trick was very simple but hard to learn. This magic show enlivened the atmosphere, and everyone enjoyed themselves, although the kids were frustrated by not being able to learn the trick. I finally taught it to them, but not without making them promise they would not teach their friends. They promised, of course.

They stayed with us until half-past eight in the evening, then kissed and hugged us goodbye. It seemed really hard for them to part. It was a little too much for me, and especially for Rivka. A little too overbearing, though we enjoyed their company very much.

Yesterday, the fundraiser event with Ariel Zilber[15] was held in Sarona. We started getting messages from everyone about how successful the event was. At some point, Izhar invited me to speak to the crowd over the phone. This brother of mine had many creative ideas in the field of communication. I spoke to the audience, saying that while the financial support was important, the knowledge that so many wonderful people were willing to donate their time and effort to help others was just as helpful. When I was done, I heard a round of enthusiastic applause. My body and soul were swept up in a tsunami of emotions.

Yet the doubts kept gnawing at me: *Was that the right way to go? Was establishing a "fundraising endeavor" of family and friends a wise choice?* Both from a medical standpoint and because of an "uncomfortable" feeling that was added to the already heavy weight I carried without much choice in the matter. On the other hand, after so much organization, preparation, and tension invested, there was a sense of great success that began to bear fruit. I suppose there was no right answer to my dilemma. This endeavor had certainly brought the family and friends closer together, especially Arieh and Dina, Izhar and Irit, Ilana, as well as many others.

Yuli was a special woman who was escorting one of the patients here—an Israeli woman from New York who had breast cancer. The patient's husband did not feel comfortable coming to the clinic, so Yuli—a woman of about fifty, who was the patient's childhood friend—volunteered to escort her during treatments at the clinic, three visits, each one three weeks long. Yuli's willingness to give up her time and energy for her childhood friend showed her kind heart and amicable personality. Yuli became widowed twenty years ago, when her husband died of terminal cancer shortly after their marriage. She had one grown daughter who was born shortly before her husband died.

With her warmth and high energy, Yuli threw a Saturday night party in the dining room with Israeli songs, in addition to others. It was amazing. She got everyone to dance, even the patients—some progressively sick. Other non-Israeli patients and caregivers joined in for what became pure ecstasy. I cannot help but think there is nothing like joy to remedy the soul. I took many pictures and had a great time.

We went back to our room around midnight and then it happened: For the first time, after many frustrating attempts, I was able to establish an internet connection on my laptop. A friend from the clinic showed me a simple technique that I could use as if I were at home in Israel. "A small step for man, a giant step for humanity..."

I took my second round of wholebody hyperthermia two days ago. I spoke to the nurse about how I went"nuts" after the treatment and how hard the recovery was for me and those around me. He promised to lower the temperature by a tenth of a degree Celsius this time around. I asked him if a tenth of a degree made any difference and he said it did. I asked him to talk to the doctor in charge about it. I think he took it as an insult to his profession, because he mumbled something unclear, but I realized he was asking me to trust him and his experience. After four or five minutes, I was fast asleep. The temperature slowly rose to a new peak of 41.9°C (107°F.)

I woke up in the recovery room toward the evening. I was still groggy but calm. I did not know where I was, what day it was, or if it was morning or night. I asked Rivka and the nurses what day it was a few times, and each time they answered me patiently. In retrospect, it seems funny to me. I slowly recovered. Rivka made sure not to let me drink in the first few hours after the treatment, but only moisten my lips with ice.

You were not allowed off the bed in the first few hours, which made the business of going to the bathroom a major project, especially when one was partly unconscious. Rivka was there for me with all her glory whenever I needed her. I think we had some heart-to-heart chats until midnight, or perhaps it was my own half-dazed mumbling. She got settled for sleeping on the armchair in the recovery room, refusing to go back to sleep in our room despite my request. However, when I woke up at some point that night, I saw she was gone. I was glad she realized there was no point in her suffering through the night.

We were in the process of packing. We were finally out of here tomorrow, and we had two main tasks ahead of us now. The first and most important one was to set up a meeting with Dr. Douwes to discuss the next treatments. It was no small matter, since he is very busy. A few days ago, we met with him and he suggested something interesting to me. He said he wanted to rehabilitate my body and made a gesture with his hand that meant sex, looking at Rivka and smiling.

He suggested we try to gradually increase the testosterone level in my body halfway, so that my disease would remain stable but my body and function would not be so deprived of the hormone. Everything would be monitored, so he said. He was not going to light a fire in a haystack, but light a small match, examine its effect, and proceed accordingly.

We finally met with him after being pulled out fifteen minutes early from a local hyperthermia treatment I was undergoing. The meeting focused on giving instructions to the doctor who wrote the summary letter he was dictating to her. Rivka was disappointed to learn that we received no information about when and how we would have to return there. I explained to her that the doctor himself did not know everything and it depended on my condition and the results of the tests I would take in Israel. If the results were good, we would not have to return. Let's hope!

We were on the flight back home. I pulled out my laptop, turned it on, and began to write. Our days with the German hosts were interesting. We were there from Friday afternoon till this morning. Rivka would have given up the experience to return home earlier. Every time we go abroad, the same thing happened. The lengthy trip began to weigh on her, and she would lose her patience and become unpleasant to be with.

I found the weekend visit to our German friends very special, particularly at night, when the kids were asleep and we had a chance to engage in some deep conversations. They worked a lot on commemorating the Holocaust. This subject matter aroused both tension and excitement in me.

Markus drove us to the airport. On the way, I told him about Rivka's experience working as a teacher in Kibbutz Lohamey Hagetaot[16] and how deeply affected her students were by their grandparents' Holocaust stories, sixty years later. The simplest things reminded them of the Holocaust, like a kibbutz fence they encountered on a trip with Rivka, or watching the electronic parts fall from the conveyer belt in the electronics factory and remembering the images of the Jews falling into the ditches after being shot. He was interested to hear that, because in their meetings, the question sometimes arises as to whether or not enough time has passed to lay this subject to rest. He told us about his wife's father, who was a soldier in the Wehrmacht[17] and fell captive, spending several years in a war prisoners' camp in France. He escaped the camp and made his way back to Germany on foot. Till today, he has terrible nightmares, and not a night passes without his waking up sweaty in the middle of the night after yelling in his sleep. Markus tried to coax him into talking at one of their family gatherings, but it nearly resulted in a catastrophe. The father hysterically yelled that Markus had no right accusing him of anything and that he owed him nothing. In all the years since then, he has never spoken to anyone about what happened to him during that terrible time. I suppose he could not free himself of the horrific crimes he committed or witnessed, and the tension releases only at night. I suggested Markus ask his father-in-law to attend one of their army unit reunions. Markus was skeptical about it. He said that to this day, they have kept their allegiance to the Reich, which means they are sworn to silence till the day they die.

We were about to land. I packed up my laptop and prepared for landing.

Hello, magnificent country.

---

15 An Israeli singer-songwriter and composer.

16 A kibbutz in northern Israel founded in 1949 by surviving fighters of the Warsaw Ghetto Uprising, as well as former Jewish partisans and other Holocaust survivors. Its name commemorates the Jews who fought the Nazis.

17 The unified armed forces of Nazi Germany from 1935–1946.

18

19

CHAPTER SIXTEEN

A FEW "SMALL" MATTERS:
LYMPHATIC MASSAGE FOR SWOLLEN LEGS

August 2004 to November 2005

After learning about the swollen leg problem at St. George Clinic in Germany and how lymphatic massage reduces the swelling, I realized I needed to continue doing it in Israel. I told Dr. Nabil about it. He had not heard of the treatment, but referred me to the physiotherapy ward. I spoke to the physiotherapist, who told me there were two expert practitioners dealing with this issue and suggested I speak to Dvora, one of them. I called her, and she invited me for a meeting.

Dvora was a pleasant, professional woman. She explained to me about all of the problems causing my limbs to swell and suggested I receive a fullbody lymphatic massage.

In our first meeting, she measured the width of my legs using a special device, so that she could monitor the changes in width throughout the treatment.

I began to see her on a weekly basis. The massage was done naked with a towel covering my private areas. The technique was a gentle "pushing" of lymphatic fluid toward my chest so it could reach the heart. Dvora began the massage in my legs, then moved to my abdominal area, and ended in my arms, with special attention given to the lymphatic glands.

Lymphatic glands are the intersections of many lymphatic vessels and serve to filter the lymphatic fluids. For example, the lymph glands in the groins store all the lymphatic fluid coming from the legs. When the fluid reaches the glands, it undergoes a filtering process, after which it continues moving upward to the heart. Some of the drainage problems are caused by an actual blockage in the glands themselves; therefore, they must be gently massaged to allow the fluid to continue flowing toward the heart.

The gentle massage had a healing quality, no doubt. It felt good. Dvora was also a good listener. We spoke quite a bit about various subjects during the treatment, some pertaining to my illness. To be honest, I did most of the talking, and she mainly listened. Sometimes, the physical relaxation allowed me to fall asleep during treatment.

One day, a guy by the name of Adi called me up. His father was an advanced prostate cancer patient. I tried to help him as best I could. Adi and his father did not know how to navigate the medical establishment efficiently or how to get his father his much-needed treatments.

Adi's father worked for the sanitation department in garbage collection and loved his job. When he began to feel bad, he went to the doctor and was diagnosed with prostate cancer metastasized in the bones. He was then referred for a trial treatment in one of the hospitals in the center of Israel. He signed the trial papers and was guaranteed to receive this treatment for three years from the date the trial began. Adi's father did not tell his family about his illness, and they did not notice the illness spreading in his body. Soon after, he received a message from the hospital that the trial had failed and his treatment stopped. He continued his hormonal treatment, which was no longer effective. Other than that, the establishment simply stopped taking care of him, and no other treatment was offered to him. Soon after, his condition deteriorated and he suffered terrible pain. The doctor prescribed him with painkiller patches. Adi, his loving son, affixed the patches on his father's back, and they alleviated the pain a little. Only at that point did the family begin to take more active involvement in their father's illness.

When Adi approached me, his father's PSA level was 300. Intense pain had spread throughout his body. The hospital disqualified him for chemo, because he had already received that treatment as part of the failed trial.

One of this man's many symptoms was significant swelling of his legs. I instructed Adi to seek lymphatic massage for his father. It took a long time until he managed to get his father to a physiotherapist specializing in lymphatic massage. By that time, his father's legs were so severely enlarged that the swelling had reached his pelvis and begun to press on sensitive organs in that region. The physiotherapist said there was nothing he could at that stage.

Apparently, neglecting this problem over time can result in unimaginable suffering and a true life risk in extreme cases. What is so astonishing about it is that the medical establishment is not aware of this common problem.

I thought that a second-line treatment, such as estrogen, might help him and ease his pain. The man's oncologist refused to prescribe this treatment, got annoyed with Adi for trying to determine what treatment his father would get. The doctor claimed it was not the right type of treatment yet offered no other solution. Adi fought for his father's right to receive the treatment, and finally, with support from other people in the establishment, his father was able to begin taking the hormone.

The treatment did wonders. Within a short time, Adi's father's PSA dropped to 150, and his pain went away completely. But the effect of the treatment only lasted about three months. The rule of thumb that one must receive treatment in the proper timing, when "the cancer is weak and the body is strong," was not kept here; therefore, its benefit was short lived. The poor state of his legs made the man's general condition even worse, and he passed away in agony shortly thereafter.

I spent about six months doing weekly lymphatic massages with Dvora. It improved the condition of my legs a lot and gradually decreased the swelling, as was clearly seen by the width measurements. As of today, I no longer need this massage, nor do I suffer from swollen legs. But I do know how to treat this symptom if it ever recurs.

THE SIDE EFFECTS OF ZOMERA

When I began my treatments with Zomera in early 2003, I knew that one of the side effects of this drug was a general bad feeling that begins a few hours after the treatment and lingers about a day or two after, mainly following the first treatment. None of the health professionals had told me about another significant side effect related to a prolonged usage of Zomera, simply because no doctors in Israel or abroad knew about it. It is hard to believe that. The phenomenon is called osteonecrosis of the jaw or in short, ONJ.

ONJ is a necrosis (gangrene) in the jawbone, usually brought on by a mouth sore that doesn't heal after a dental procedure that exposed the jawbone in some way, such as tooth extraction. This necrosis that doesn't heal becomes a spot that attracts infection and causes pain inside the mouth. This may result in severe damage to the patient's quality of life or even threaten his life if the necrosis spreads, in which case no treatment is known to help—not sterilization, antibiotics, etc.

Apparently, this necrosis phenomenon occurs mainly among patients who have used Zomera over a long term and especially those who have used it frequently. Moreover, stopping the use of Zomera, even for a few years, does not reduce the chance of contracting ONJ, since the drug remains in the bones for a very long time. According to what is known today, the risk is gone only a decade after stopping the use of this drug. But cumulative data shows that the risk of suffering from ONJ diminishes along with decreased Zomera usage.

The preliminary findings regarding this phenomenon were published as early as mid-2004. During 2006, more new information about ONJ was published in articles and on the patients' online forum. One of the forum members—a dentist and cancer patient, of course—began to research this phenomenon in depth and published his findings in a summarized article featuring photos of damage to the oral cavity among some patients. It looked and sounded bad.

The only treatment for this phenomenon is a preventive one. Zomera users must avoid, as much as possible, any dental procedures related to exposing the jaw bone. A patient who is destined to use Zomera should first get his dental treatments done, and even a preventive one. If there is a need for extraction, dentures, or any other treatment that requires exposure of the jawbone, it is highly important to perform it before the first Zomera treatment.

Those who have already been treated with Zomera should maintain oral hygiene and take preventive treatments to prevent any dental work that might cause the onset of ONJ.

I was a "heavy user" of Zomera, almost addicted to it. I had been receiving this drug by IV for about three years. I realized I had to address this phenomenon with all seriousness.

I consulted Dr. Bassam about ONJ and sent him material on the topic. All he said was, "More is hidden than is revealed." In simple words, I did not gain anything from talking to him on this topic.

I told Dr. Raviv, my dentist, about the phenomenon and about my personal interest in it and sent him some information. He did not know anything about it either. At first he thought it was an "esoteric, marginal phenomenon." A short while later, he called and told me that ever since I brought ONJ to his attention, he checked and found that the professional literature contained many reports and articles on the topic. Dr. Raviv added that there was a dental conference coming up in Jerusalem that was fully dedicated to this subject. I decided to attend. I thought it would be good if Dr. Raviv did too, but that didn't happen.

I went alone. Most of the participants were dentists and representatives from dental equipment suppliers. I wondered how to introduce myself. I didn't want to identify myself as a patient, so I decided to put on the good old engineer suit and look dignified. However, I still found myself having to explain to few people here and there, who wondered about my presence, why I was interested in the conference.

The large video screen at the conference showed pictures of patients suffering from ONJ. This "small matter" seemed terrible when projected on a large screen. No words can describe the severity of utter rotting inside a person's mouth.

Dr. Raviv put together a preventive treatment plan for me. The main components were a panoramic photo of all my teeth in order to get a current diagnosis and a semiannual appointment with a professional hygienist for plaque removal and general checkup. This was usually done by a hygienist, but Dr. Raviv took it on himself, so that there would be no risk of random damage to my jawbone. These visits also provided information about the condition of my teeth and any other necessary procedures. We have stuck to this plan over the years. With Dr. Raviv's instruction, I have maintain proper oral hygiene, and there is an added value to it—my teeth are in top form.

With Dr. Bassam's consent, we decided to reduce the frequency of my Zomera treatment. We both thought it appropriate to take a break. Ever since I had become aware of ONJ, I gradually decreased the frequency of receiving the Zomera IV. At first it went down to once every two months, and we next dropped it to once every three months. So far, so good. Nothing bad happened as a result of this reduction; it simply meant I was letting fewer chemicals into my system.

CHAPTER SEVENTEEN

THE NOOSE LOOSENS

September 2007

The human body is such a phenomenal machine that it can fix its own malfunctions. Top engineers could not have invented such a sophisticated machine.

I am gradually returning to life. My physical condition is slowly improving. My medical indices are good and stable. Everything is lining up in my body and I am once more on the racetrack of life.

My PSA continuously show a zero. This is the aspiration of every prostate cancer patient. The stability of the indices is no less important than the value of the index itself. This indicates a constant, unchanging state. In the medical jargon, they call it remission. The term "remission" does not quite represent my condition. Remission alludes to a temporary state, and according to its definition, at some point it will stop and my illness will attack once more. I do not accept this definition, and as far as myself and my illness are concerned, I am clear—it is a constant state and will never change for the rest of my life.

Yes, I am still under periodic treatments, mainly with Zomera, which means that every three months, I visit the oncological unit and receive this sneaky substance by IV. Bone metastases that are not properly treated may cause fractures. It is hard to describe the suffering that those patients with bone fractures in their pelvis or spine experience due to metastases in these areas. This eventually shortens their lives. Zomera treatments help these patients tremendously by minimizing this phenomenon. Aside from Zomera, I take vitamin D and calcium daily as part of my maintenance.

Vitamin D is naturally produced in our bodies, aided by sunlight that hits exposed parts. People above fifty produce less vitamin D, especially those who are rarely exposed to the sun. (In fact, most Westerners get minimal exposure to the sun.) Vitamin D has a highly significant function in our body. It helps the absorption of calcium in our bones. Calcium deficiency in the bones is known as osteoporosis, a phenomenon that causes depletion of the bone mass in the body, especially among older people and women in menopause.

The direct result of osteoporosis among older people is that bones are more fragile and can break.

In order to prevent or at least reduce this unpleasant phenomenon, older people should take vitamin D and calcium as regular supplements. Patients with bone metastases are much more prone to this phenomenon, since some of the malignant processes in the bones cause significant osteoporosis, and if it is not properly treated, it may cause fractures in the metastasized areas.

The blood tests I take as part of my follow-up on the various parameters has shown an excess of TSH (thyroid stimulating hormone). This may be attributed to some hormonal imbalance due to the various treatments I have gone through. To balance this hormone, my trusted family doctor has recommended I take one Eltroxin pill a day. This indeed stabilized my TSH level to its recommended value, allowing me to overcome one more obstacle.

A metastasized cancer patient's illness is defined as symptomatic. It means that there are many odd phenomena that are not directly linked to the illness, but may attack the patient through various systems of the body. Thus, many cancer patients with metastases are exposed to the risk of blood clots in the deep veins of the legs (DVT), which I have mentioned earlier. Research shows that about 20 percent of cancer patients die from blood clots rather than cancer itself. These blood clots disconnect from their area and flow freely through the bloodstream, possibly creating a kind of stopper that blocks the blood flow to the heart, lungs, or brain so that it becomes a life threat. To reduce this risk, one must take blood thinners. Coumadin is one example of blood thinner while aspirin is another, yet the latter works through a different mechanism.

When I realized the importance of blood thinning in my case, I consulted a few doctors and even an expert hematologist on using Coumadin. Neither of them explicitly recommended using it, though they did not deny the problem of blood clotting. It seems odd to me. Why would they not recommend a drug that can save lives? Now I understand that doctors are afraid of over-thinning the blood and internal bleeding. (Such bleeding damaged former Israeli Prime Minister Ariel Sharon after he received blood thinners to ensure the dissolving of a blood clot that had harmed him a few days prior to that.) The degree of blood thinning can be tested in a simple blood test called INR. When the INR result is 1, it means that the blood-thinning level is normal, as in a healthy person. When the INR level is 3 or over, the blood is too thin and there is a risk of internal bleeding. The doctors I have consulted about using Coumadin refrained from approving my usage of the drug. I suppose they are worried about overuse of Coumadin and the risk of bleeding. They do not trust a patient to ensure he takes the proper dose of Coumadin to regulate his INR level to the desired value. Dr. Charles Myers's suggestion was to take a low dose of Coumadin to prevent the occurrence of blood clots. He has also recommended a periodic testing of the INR level in my blood. I have decided to add Coumadin to my personal drug basket, while ensuring I take periodic INR tests, along with all the other blood tests I take for my regular follow-up.

I also take a few other pills that may be helping me fight the cancer. Lycopene, the red pigment found in tomatoes and other red fruits, is known to have anticancer properties in prostate cancer cases. Countless articles have been written about its beneficial properties. Up until recently, I would take one lycopene pill every morning. But a more recent article published argued that there is no proof of lycopene's benefits, so I am not sure if I should continue taking it or not.

I also take a selenium pill everyday. Selenium is a mineral found in various concentrations in the ground in different areas of the world. Research relating to it has found that in areas where selenium concentration is high, there are less cases of prostate cancer. Hence, the conclusion is that selenium intake leads to a reduction in prostate cancer development.

Similarly, I take omega-3 fatty acids on a daily basis.

The parameter that seems to most affect my health is testosterone. Among prostate cancer patients, testosterone is a double-edged sword in every sense of the word. On the one hand, the presence of testosterone accelerates the spreading of cancer, so that patients, especially those with metastasized prostate cancer, must maintain a very low level of testosterone to try and curb the disease. On the other hand, long-term testosterone deficiency causes negative side effects in many of the body's systems. It is known that a low level of testosterone interferes with sexual urge, but there are other negative side effects, such as memory loss, weight gain, muscle atrophy, osteoporosis, constant fatigue as part of a rundown physical state, and more. I have studied this topic, and in my case, found a direct link between low testosterone level and higher sugar level, so much so that I risked becoming diabetic. I have also found that blood count, immune system, hemoglobin level, and TSH level are also directly dependent upon the level of testosterone in the body. When my testosterone level is low, my sugar level hikes and my blood count drops. And when my testosterone level is high, sugar drops and blood count improves, as does general feeling in all parts of my body.

The emotional–behavioral aspect must also be mentioned. I have learned that testosterone deficiency also affects a patient's behavior. It is known that men with high levels of testosterone are more active and perhaps more aggressive than men with low testosterone. The latter seem gentler and less prone to arguments and clashes, forgoing things more easily and avoiding conflicts. Have I adopted these qualities while my testosterone was low? Has my behavior become more conceding? The idea that testosterone level changes my overall behavior frustrates me, not to mention how it might affect my business conduct. Another interesting question, for which I have no answer, is, what would have changed in my life had my testosterone level remained the same before the cancer erupted?

We, the patients, feel the ramifications of treatments offered by expert doctors in our bodies and souls. Often, the doctor is not aware of all the side effects caused by a treatment he prescribes. When asking to stop hormonal treatment, I was once asked by the oncologist in response: "What is actually bothering you?" These phenomena are so complicated that I did not even know where to start. No one but the patient himself can truly understand how these experiences feel.

As said, testosterone affects various body systems so much so that a technique was developed to consciously take breaks from hormonal treatments for certain periods of time. This technique is especially suitable for non-metastasized, local cancer. When PSA drops to about zero and stabilizes for nearly a year, hormonal treatment is stopped to enable a patient's body to reactivate the production of testosterone. The break in treatment and gradual increase of testosterone allows the patient's systems to recover as he enjoys an improved quality of life during that period. The duration of the break is determined by PSA level. As soon the PSA rears its ugly head and begins to hike, it means one thing only—that the disease is spreading through the body once again, and that hormonal treatment must be resumed to decrease testosterone in the body and suppress the scum once more.

Dr. Charles Myers writes in his book that low testosterone over a long period of time poses a real threat to a patients' health during hormonal treatments.

The issue of low testosterone has kept me preoccupied. I feel the deficiency in this hormone. It has been at a minimal level in my body for a few years now, and I am aware of the destructive effect this has on my health, down to a real life threat. At the same time, the deficiency in testosterone is what disables the scum from rearing its head again. I still debate in this matter. I need to make another decision that will affect the course of my life. I have shared my dilemma with Rivka. Naturally, her opinion was equivocal, but in her own way, she let me understand that it was worth the try.

As part of my attempts, I decided to conduct a clinical trial with just one patient—myself—to try to improve the quality of my life. I promised myself I would be extremely cautious. I studied the subject and discovered that there is a testosterone gel you can rub on your stomach that gets absorbed through the skin. Thus, I found myself one night after my shower applying this good but dangerous substance on my stomach with shaky hands.

The alcohol in the gel evaporates quickly, especially if you blow on it. The testosterone itself remains on the stomach and slowly gets absorbed.

I did not know how much to rub in. I was afraid to apply too much and raise my testosterone level too quickly. I decided to take the trial-and-error route. This is method I have learned during my life as an engineer for how to handle subject matters for which you have no information but can assess the error by trying different things.

After a few days of rubbing the gel on my stomach, and as part of this "trial and error," I went to take some blood tests, including ones for testosterone and PSA. I was hoping the testosterone would be within the norm of a healthy person, and that the PSA would remain zero. The test results indeed showed a testosterone level any Israeli man would be proud of, and the PSA remained zero. I noted to myself: *The testosterone won—1:0.* Dr. Ruby explained to me that at some point, once the testosterone rose, so did the PSA, as if it were testosterone's shadow. Still, I realized that between the rise of testosterone and the appearance of its "shadow," there was a certain time gap.

A few days later, when I was at the dairy, I suddenly felt very bad. I was dizzy and weak throughout my body with such intensity that I could not drive home. I called Rivka and asked her to pick me up. I thought that this "crisis" had to do with the sharp hormonal change I underwent. I decided to stop using testosterone. That, too, was a mistake. The testosterone plummeted fast, and I felt dizzy and weak once again.

Later on, when the unpleasant sensation subsided, I decided to resume testosterone use. I began to rub the gel on my stomach nightly, but this time I applied a smaller amount each time. Slowly but surely, using the trial-anderror method and after measuring the testosterone and PSA rather frequently, I finally understood how this mechanism acts. My testosterone rose. It was still somewhat lower than the norm, but this level upgraded all of my bodily systems significantly.

But as expected, after about two months with a zero reading, the PSA reared its head and began to rise. According to the theory I have adopted, I did not want the cancer to gain momentum, so I immediately stopped using the gel. Since the testosterone was not very high in my blood at that point, I did not experience the same horrible feeling. My PSA reacted as expected—it dropped back to zero. Another point in my favor.

I am learning to control this matter. I enjoy the testosterone, even if not fully and constantly, but it is still an improvement in my condition. The price I pay for this is constantly being on watch; every time the PSA rears its head, I must stop using the gel.

What have I learned from this is something I should have already known: You cannot change your body's hormone level so rapidly.

The periodic bloodwork I do shows considerable improvement in all the above mentioned indices—my immune system as reflected in my white blood cells, hemoglobin, sugar, and TSH.

My general feeling also has improved significantly. I feel that my circulation is better and my body responds to my wishes more easily. My overall energy level has increased, and my inner engine works more efficiently and vigorously. I do not know if my behavior is changing due to the rise of testosterone. I cannot point to any change in this regard.

But as expected, after about two months with a zero reading, the PSA reared its head and began to rise. According to the theory I had adopted, I did not want the cancer to gain momentum, so I immediately stopped using the gel. Since the testosterone was not very high in my blood at that point, I did not experience the same horrible feeling. My PSA reacted as expected—it dropped back to zero. Another point in my favor. I am learning to control this matter. I enjoy the testosterone, even if not fully and constantly, but it is still an improvement in my condition. The price I pay for this is constantly being on watch; every time the PSA rears its head, I must stop using the gel.

Using testosterone has become a routine for me. I make sure to measure the hormone and PSA in the required frequency. It is a cat-and-mouse game, and I am the mouse: I must remain alert and not let the cat attack me and tear me to pieces.

Does this method further enhance my personal battle against cancer? Am I keeping the cancer curbed and suppressed by hitting it as soon as it peeks through, while it is still small and weak? Does this treatment method disable the cancer from developing AI mutations that are resistant to the hormonal treatment?

Of course, I have no answers to these questions, but deep inside, I want to believe that it is so, and that this treatment significantly contributes to my war against the scum and improves my quality of life.

To this day, I have not heard about any prostate cancer patient who does that. I may be the first one to take such a therapeutic approach.

At the same time, I maintain a low-fat diet rich in fruit and vegetables. Most of the experts believe that proper nutrition is a key to better health. I believe it, too. We have stopped eating fried foods. French fries and the like are *casus belli* in our house. Rivka has become an expert on cooking without oil. We try to eat whole wheat products, brown rice, and the least amount of sugar. I eat hummus and vegetables for lunch at Danny's Hummus Place in Nahariya instead of the *schwarma*[18] and falafel I once ate.

Physical activity also contributes to health and feeling good. I try to do it daily, walking uphill to the top of my street and back every morning. It stimulates blood flow and rejuvenates me before my workday at the dairy begins. I bought a bike, which I ride on from the Ben-Ami village to Nahariya and back. It leaves me feeling healthy and great physically.

Over the years since I have been diagnosed, my path as a cancer patient has converged with those of many other patients with metastasized cancer. Many of them are no longer alive. Bill Aishman was an advanced-stage prostate cancer patient who I met through the online forum I had joined. Bill was a researcher, an autodidact of the highest order. He studied prostate cancer and the treatments offered to patients in depth and gathered his findings in many articles which he had published on the website.

Bill was the oracle on the forum. Patients would address any tough question regarding prostate cancer and metastases to him, asking for his opinion. I am well aware that the idea of pursuing chemo at the onset of my battle came from him. He himself wrote that he regretted not implementing this idea on himself. The idea of intentionally stopping chemo was also something I learned from him. Therefore, in some way, I can say that he is the one who saved my life.

Bill defined so well our goal as prostate cancer patients with metastases—since our illness is not fully curable, we must aspire to turn it into a chronic disease, so that as such, it does not lead to death and we can continue our daily lives using proper treatment. I am fulfilling his vision. I receive the adequate treatment and live my life normally and with quality.

— ◊ —

I have developed a healthy man's routine. I work full time. While I do not engage in significant physical labor, I have no other limitation.

I have decided to try to live the rest of my life in the best way possible, and I have turned this desire into a principle. I try and succeed in enjoying life as much as I can.

I have broken free from the heavy burden I carried on my shoulders. Unlike before, the cancer no longer weighs deeply on my soul. I am no longer jealous of anyone. I walk down the street with pride, I look good, my chest is lifted, and I bounce as I walk, like athletes do. I am proud of my stride and my good health.

My success in battling cancer has spread among different circles. I have written about a few topics pertaining to the illness for the "shalom prostate" website established by my friend, Lenny. I added my name and email address, as well as my phone number. Bit by bit, patients began to come to me for advice. Everyone wants to copy my success. I have become a partial guru.

The oncologist working under the medical establishment in Israel usually treats a fairly large number of different cancer diseases. Thus, he cannot develop a high level of knowledge and expertise I believe is needed in order to optimally treat and achieve the best possible results. In my mind, having an oncologist focus on one type of cancer and learn about it in depth, including all its aspects and possible treatments, can lead to an optimal treatment of patients and to successfully fighting this complex disease.

Dr. Charles Myers, who I have gotten to know through the prostate cancer online forum, is one such example. He is an oncological expert on prostate cancer only. Many patients have mentioned his unique expertise and how much he has helped them. He also expressed his opinions in the forum every so often. Over the years, I have asked him questions pertaining to myself and my illness. His answers have been somewhat laconic, but they helped me reach decisions about how to proceed with my treatment. I am very impressed with his knowledge, especially by his holistic approach. More than just a direct treatment of prostate cancer, he prescribes a life style that includes proper nutrition and an emphasis on a patient's general condition, while taking into consideration the general parameters of the patient's health and any other background illnesses he might have. Dr. Myers heads a private institute for prostate cancer research and has spent all of his professional life on it.

Dr. Myers has another important quality that can be called "spirit." He tries to instill in his patients a renewed spirit, which I would describe as letting a patient know that he is receiving the highest level of treatment that can bring him long-term relief. This quality is very important to patients, especially those with terminal illnesses.

The irony is that he was diagnosed with prostate cancer himself and his condition was fairly severe by then. Despite his expertise, he decided not to handle his mode of treatment himself. He felt that he might not be objective enough or make the right decisions about how to treat himself. So he turned to his colleagues, and together they outlined his treatment method. Today, his condition is good and his disease is in deep remission.

I was asked to speak to another support group near Tel Aviv. I invited Dr. Avivit to the meeting, assuming she would not show up. I was right. Doctors do not usually view their patients as equals on professional matters.

At the end of the meeting, a couple around my age, named Ilan and Ronit, approached and asked if they could speak to me. That morning, they went to Avivit and found out that Ilan had prostate cancer that had metastasized to his lungs and lymph glands. In her own unique way, Avivit hinted to them that Ilan did not stand much of a chance, or as she put it to Ronit, "His clock is ticking." When they reached me, they were emotionally wrecked and searching for something to hang on to.

About 80 percent of metastasized prostate cancer cases end up with bone metastases. The remaining percentage has metastases in the lymph glands. Prostate cancer with lung metastases is very rare. I assumed that none of the oncologists in Israel had ever encountered lung metastases in prostate cancer, and if they had—they probably did not have the skills required to successfully treat it.

As a result, I reached a decision that the best advice I could give to Ilan and Ronit was to tell them about Dr. Charles Myers and recommended that Ilan become his patient.

The decision to become a patient of an overseas doctor is not simple and is not for everyone. The patient must be an active type, who is determined and willing to fight for his life, and is able to handle the project emotionally, physically, and financially.

My impression of Ilan and Ronit was that they were suitable for that. Their relationship was strong. I knew they would not rule out treatment overseas outright. I asked Ilan what he did for a living. He said humbly that he worked at a food packing factory. I happen to know this factory from my dairy business.

Ilan and Ronit did not accept my advice immediately, but we got along well and agreed to stay in touch. Our acquaintance quickly developed into friendship. I found Ilan to be a charming man. I inquired about his job at the factory in our second meeting, and he said he was the manager. On our third meeting, I found out he was the owner of the factory. I told him, "Listen, in our first meeting, you were the worker. In the second, you were the manager, and in the third, you were the owner! I wonder where you will get to in out next meeting."

Ilan began to receive chemo in a hospital in Israel along with hormonal treatment. Soon after, he contacted Dr. Myers to seek further treatment with him. The doctor sent him a questionnaire of twenty-three pages about his medical condition. He suggested that Ilan be accompanied by his own doctor for their first meeting, so that he could help him tackle the professional issues. Ilan kept me in the loop. He had a hard time recruiting a doctor to join him in the meeting. Finally, he asked me to accompany him. I felt flattered.

By chance, I was supposed to visit the United States around the same time for a food show in New York. My son, Orr, was about to complete his military service. I offered for him to join me, seeing it as a perfect opportunity to spend some quality time with my eldest son.

Ilan and Ronit picked me up on a rainy day from a Starbucks in Doylestown, Pennsylvania. Orr went to New York City on his own to spend some time in the Big Apple. We agreed to meet three days later. I thought, *Wow, my son is all grown up and becoming a citizen of the world.*

Toward the evening, we arrived at Earlysville, where Dr. Myers's clinic was located. After stopping overnight at a hotel, we arrived at the institute in the late hours of the morning. The institute was located in a remote area at the edge of town inside a dense wood.

A polite secretary welcomed us and led us to a prestigious waiting area. The doctor entered after some time. We shook hands politely, and he invited Ilan for a physical exam that lasted more than twenty minutes. I mentioned to Ronit how thorough he seemed—taking so long to examine Ilan after having received a twenty-three-page questionnaire!

To the best of my knowledge, no doctor in Israel verifies so thoroughly a patient's details or examines him for that long. They do not have time for that, and perhaps it is not customary in our culture.

At the end of the examination, the secretary invited us in. Dr. Myers analyzed Ilan's medical condition in detail, explaining the series of treatments he proposed. He took into consideration all of Ilan's medical parameters and custom-tailored him a treatment based on Ilan's physical condition. In general, the doctor suggested two second-line hormonal treatment drugs, in addition to supporting drugs that invigorated the body's immune system. The hormonal treatments Dr. Myers offered Ilan included estrogen and Nizoral.

Estrogen is the female sex hormone. In the last decades, it has been known to fight prostate cancer effectively. In the middle of last century, it was given to prostate cancer patients in the form of oral pills called DES. Studies aimed at examining the efficiency of the drug have found that many of the patients died during treatment. As a result, the therapy was stopped almost entirely. Years after the treatment was dropped, it turned out that the reason for the high mortality among patients was not prostate cancer but blood clots (deep vein thrombosis, or DVT in short) caused by the drug in the patients' leg veins. These clots sometimes detach from their area and move with the blood flow. As I mentioned earlier, such blood clots may be a life threat—as they were among many patients who took this drug with its strong anticancer activity, which indeed suppressed the cancer but caused some deaths due to blood clots. Once the cause for patients' deaths was clarified, the drug was put back into use, but this time accompanied by blood thinners, prevent DVT.

A breakthrough in this field in recent years is the use of estrogen patches. These are affixed to the skin, and the hormone gets absorbed directly through it. Menopausal women are the main target audience for these patches, which are designed to reduce side effects of menopause, such as hot flashes and osteoporosis. The patches' advantage is that the hormone does not pass through the digestive system or blood flow, thus the chance of forming blood clots is low.

The second drug Ilan was prescribed, Nizoral, was originally used as an anti-fungal medication, but has proven to be highly effective against prostate cancer.

Despite the proven activity of these drugs in fighting prostate cancer, doctors in Israel hardly ever offer them to prostate cancer patients. I do not know why. Perhaps they do not know enough about them? Or maybe the drugs are too cheap and no pharmacy will earn enough by selling them; therefore, no one promotes them?

Today, Ilan is still treated by Dr. Myers, three years after he was diagnosed as a prostate cancer patient with metastases in the lungs and lymph glands. Despite the grave forecast he was given, he is in top form. His PSA level is very close to zero, the metastases are no longer seen in the CT tests, and he feels wonderful. He lives a full life like many other healthy people his age.

Over time, I have referred other patients who have reached a dead end with the treatment they received in Israel to Dr. Myers. Among them were patients whose illnesses were complex and to whom I thought he could bring relief.

— ◊ —

A few months ago, about twenty of us—all prostate cancer patients—got together at Ilan's house. Some of our wives were present, as well. It was one of the first meetings we dedicated to establishing a prostate cancer patients' association. Since, we did not all know each other prior to the meeting, we took turns introducing ourselves briefly. After I introduced myself, Ilan added that I saved his life. Next, Dan, who I had helped, introduced himself, saying I saved his life, too. I was surprised and embarrassed at the same time, but the more I think about it today, the more I am proud. After all, how many people in our world can hear from other people that they have saved their lives? I suppose doctors hear that often from their patients, but unlike me, it is their occupation and professional vocation in life.

In 2005, a conference was held that dealt with the latest innovations in treating cancer. I decided to attend the conference. It was held in one of the fancy hotels in the diamond district near Tel Aviv. Most of the participants were doctors and people whose occupation involved cancer. Like everyone else, I was asked at the reception for my occupation. They print it on the conference tag you wore. I debated how to present myself. *Should I say I am a cheesemaker? This would probably elicit some amazement and smiles. Or perhaps I should introduce myself as a cancer patient*? This infamous title seemed just as undesirable to me. I decided to recruit my old engineer suit once more and become a mechanical engineer for one day. It was factually true, and perhaps an engineer had things in common with the professional matters presented in the conference. Even this title aroused some questions, but I made sure to keep it vague enough.

Sasson Ben Shimon is an organic chemistry professor at the Hebrew University in Jerusalem. The subject matter of his lecture intrigued me and led me to attend the conference. The logic behind this new anticancer treatment he had developed seemed true to me. It involved two principles whose power I acknowledged. The first principle is the angiogenesis principle I have mentioned earlier.

His innovation is that the drug works to inhibit five different angiogenic mechanisms, hindering the development of new blood vessels that supply oxygen and nutrients to the cancerous cells, thus allowing their destructive development in five different ways. The older generations of angiogenic drugs, such as thalidomide, attack those same blood vessels with only one mechanism.

The second principle is synergy, whose power I greatly believe in. It is obvious that attacking the disease with five different mechanisms at the same time may yield better results than attacking five mechanisms, each at different times.

Moreover, the treatment does not seem to have severe side effects and is done at home by the patient himself.

Cancer is a shrewd, sophisticated disease that manages to override many drugs that pure logic claims can destroy it. The problem is that in real life, the disease finds ways to bypass a drug's effect and continue to develop despite the drug's presence. Therefore, attacking the development mechanism of new blood vessels with five different tools simultaneously seemed interesting to me

The lecture left a great impression on me. Bill Aishman, of blessed memory, defined the goal of turning cancer from a terminal disease to a chronic disease. Could this antiangiogenic treatment turn the disease to a chronic one? Could the patient taking these drugs be able to live his life like a normal person?

Naturally, these questions have yet to be answered. I thought it appropriate that other prostate cancer patients I know, especially those whose disease is progressive, hear about and get to know this treatment method, especially since the professor was about to begin clinical trials on humans. I thought that patients who had exhausted common treatments and had no other solution would be interested in participating. I organized two meetings between Professor Ben Shimon and the patients. One of them was held at Ilan's house and other one in his factory's conference room. The professor was a modest, pleasant man. He knew how to relay his messages so they would reach every person. He managed to fascinate the patients and give new hope to these people whose lives depended on curbing the disease.

At that time, my friend, Shmuel, was one of those people. His condition was pretty bad, and his appearance gave away the disease progressing in his body. His face was red, his temperature regulation system went off, and he had to wear a coat when it was not at all cold outside. His PSA hiked to 3,000, and all the common treatments no longer worked.

Shmuel had a huge body and soul. He worked in the railway authority for many years. When he was about fifty-three, he discovered traces of blood in his urine. Naturally, he went to see a urologist at the local health clinic, who sent him for general tests that did not include a PSA, for some reason. For the blood in his urine, Shmuel was given an anti-infection treatment. Shmuel had blood in his urine for six months. During that time, the disease continued to spread in his body and he had pain in his bones. Realizing the urologist would not solve his problem, and seeing that his condition was deteriorating, Shmuel and his wife decided to get a second opinion. They turned to a urologist in another health clinic branch in Haifa. Upon arriving and taking a PSA test, the frightening result was 700. This meant beyond any doubt that the disease had metastasized in his body and spread widely into his bones. Just like that, Shmuel became a severe patient.

The chemo worked well to curb Shmuel's disease. His big, strong body helped him absorb the huge amounts of chemo he received during those years. So much so, that it almost passed unnoticed on his body.

There was no doubt that not many could have withstood so much chemotherapy.

After about four years, the treatment was no longer effective, and his disease broke out again. Now Shmuel had to find an alternative treatment.

Shmuel's eyes lit up when he heard about Ben Shimon's new treatment approach. He asked to participate in the trial and was referred by the professor to the hospital that was about to execute the trial. But in the blood tests he took before the starting the trial, they discovered that the disease had reached the circulatory system so much so that his participation was disqualified. It was a sad moment. Shmuel and his family knew that their last treatment option had escaped them. He was a pleasant, amicable man. I liked getting together with him. He told me about the details of his disease and about the claim he had filed against the health services to be compensated for the medical negligence in his case. I was glad when he told me he had won the claim and received considerable monetary compensation. The money would help his family recover after his death.

I called him shortly after finding out he was disqualified for the new treatment. He suffered great pain and had to use a walker to move around the house. He asked me if I had any other tricks up my sleeve. My eyes welled up with tears. I did not even have a half a trick. Shmuel died shortly thereafter. I did not attend the funeral. A month later, his wife invited me to take part in his memorial. I did not go, and I feel guilty about it from time to time. Blessed be his memory.

Sadly, there were other less fortunate cases.

I never spoke to Bill Aishman, a long-distance close friend from the forum, but he helped me make significant decisions about treating my disease, and his advice played a considerable part in my survival. But I never had a chance to tell him that. He himself did not survive. He passed away about eight years after being diagnosed with a PSA level of 300 and a Gleason score of 9. He spent much of that time in chemotherapy, until his disease developed resistance to all types of chemo available.

Robert Young, the man who developed the prostate cancer glossary, passed away after his PSA had gone up to 1,200. Robert, who got married a second time six months before he died, asked his wife to burn his body and scatter his ashes in the Gulf of Mexico, in memory of his days as a seaman and because he loved the sea so much. The website containing the glossary he wrote has helped me a great deal in understanding the myriad new definitions I had to learn about my illness. The website has helped patients and their families for years after his death.

Larry Sorenson, my Australian friend who sent me my first chemo protocol by email, also passed away. Thanks to him, I realized that his protocol was the right one for me. He never knew about the excellent outcome that treatment had on me. He also did not know how much he dispersed my concerns about the side effects of the treatment, thanks to the way in which he described how the course of treatment fared with him and the relatively mild side effects he experienced.

Many patients call me. They all want to succeed like me. I help them as best as I can, telling them among other things about the chemo protocol I underwent. They ask me to send it to them. The name given to that chemo protocol among the patients' community is "the Australian protocol." Sometimes, a patient calls and simply asks me to send him "the Australian protocol." I realize that he does not know why the protocol is called by that name.

Don Cooley, who founded and managed the cancer patients' online forum, shut it down. He did not have enough strength to go on after most of the friends, who helped him establish and run the forum, passed away and left him almost alone. Today, you can read the abundance of material about prostate cancer, but the forum that was active and lively, if you can call it that way, is no longer alive. Those who wish to, can find the material in the following URL: Prostate-help.org.

Bob was a Scottish man of about forty-five when he discovered he had metastasized prostate cancer. His father was also sick with the same cancer at the same time. Bob had an Israeli girlfriend. Despite or in spite of his illness, they decided to get married and move to Israel. They said that in Israel, the medical care was better than in Scotland. When Bob arrived with his new wife in 2005 to meet Lenny and me at the Ben-Ami dairy, he was deeply depressed by his illness. We tried, and even succeeded to a great extent, to lift him out of his depression. We explained to him that metastasized cancer was not a death sentence. I was the living example. That did the trick. Bob gathered himself up and began chemotherapy shortly thereafter. The chemo consisted of Taxotere once every three weeks. His body responded amazingly to the treatment, and his illness retreated dramatically. He was reborn. Bob, who was an amateur marathon runner, had an athlete's body. At the end of his chemo, he went back to running and even participated in the London marathon.

Shortly thereafter, the illness broke out in his body once more. He was put back on chemotherapy, but the illness was stronger than him and kept spreading despite the treatment. I spoke to him when he was hospitalized. He was weak and died a few days later.

From among the Israeli patients we met at St. George clinic in Germany, twelve passed away from other types of cancer. Aside from me, there is only one other patient still with us, but her condition is not good.

Over the years, I have asked myself every so often, *what has happened with me? Why did I win*? Despite all the diagnoses and prognoses, I am alive today and functioning like a healthy person, more than seven years after being diagnosed as a terminal patient whose days were numbered.

True, I have not been cured; I live in an odd symbiosis with the cancer. Yet, what makes me different than all the other patients whose bodies did not endure and who surrendered to this terrible disease? Naturally, this is a complex matter with many aspects to it that lacks any clear answer. However, I do have plenty of assumptions.

I once met with an oncologist as part of a medical conference. He wanted to know what I thought contributed to my great condition when my prognosis was so terrible. I lectured to him about one of my assumptions that I thought fit the occasion. I have mentioned this theory already. Prostate cancer contains two types of malignant cells: AD (androgen dependent), which are sensitive to hormonal treatment and are suppressed by it, thus suppressing the cancer; and AI (androgen independent) cells, which are resistant to hormonal treatment, thus allowing the cancer to spread despite hormonal treatment. Therefore, patients who carry these murderous AI cells in their body may suffer from a disease that spreads despite hormonal treatment, until death.

I told that oncologist that I believed my chemo completely destroyed the AI cells in my body; therefore, I could cope with the AD cells by taking hormonal treatment only. The oncologist was deeply impressed by my general understanding and theory. It was no doubt flattering, though, of course, I did not invent this theory but learned it from my teacher in the forum—the great Bill Aishman of blessed memory.

Of course, this is not the only reason for my success in this battle.

I believe that the combination between the hormonal, chemotherapy, conventional, and alternative treatments has helped me with the battle. The many blows my cancer received, in the "way of the cat", when the weak cat serves the strong snake a series of quick, small blows, has destroyed it, at least for now..

Naturally, there are many other parameters in this complex equation.

Had I not been blessed with a supportive environment—namely my wonderful family, friends, doctors who stood by my side, and all the others who enlisted to support me—I would not have survived.

Another clear insight and perhaps the most important one, which slowly penetrated my mind over time, is that I would not have survived without being an "active patient. "If I were a "conformist"who stayed on the path outlined to me by the medical establishment, I would have, no doubt, aligned with the somber predictions that gave me a lifespan of less than two years. In reality, these are true.

Conformist—a person who acts according to the accepted rules in his environment. When there is a contrast between his own cognition and the acceptable codes of behavior around him, he will opt to be accepted.

— ◊ —

Nobody in the medical establishment asks, checks, or verifies the reasons for which I am still alive today, contradictory to the "fairly bad prognosis" as defined by Avivit at that time, and in opposition to any known statistics. No one from the system that cares for me realizes that perhaps the steps taken to treat me and my disease are worth reviewing, perhaps they will be of help to other patients so they can change their verdict. And can the myriad treatments I received and that have proven successful in me be duplicated in other cases? And perhaps I expect too much of the establishment.

---

18 Gyro-style shredded meat made of lamb or turkey.

CHAPTER EIGHTEEN
THE GRAND FINALE

September 25, 2008

Orr called from Be'er Sheba and suggested we all go to Paul McCartney's concert in Tel Aviv. I obliged happily. I was a teenager in the sixties when the Beatles became mega-stars. They were my idols when I was a teenager. I jumped at the opportunity to spend an exciting evening with my children. Orr's offer flattered me. After all, it's not everyday that a young twenty-fouryear-old invites his fifty-six-year-old father to spend an evening with him. It was his birthday, too. I had spoken to him about it and said the concert would be his birthday present.

Rivka did not want to come—the crowdedness and pressure didn't suit her—and Guri was in the army. It was just Orr, Bat-El, and me.

We arrived at the park before five in the afternoon, about three hours before the concert was set to begin. We sat on the lawn outside the concert area and ate some snacks Orr brought with him. About thirty minutes before the show, they allowed us into the fenced area, and we saw people rushing to get good spots near the stage. It was a funny sight. After all, there was room for tens of thousands of people. It reminded me of the sheep herd in Sarona running to the water trough to quench their thirst after a hot day in the meadow.

Shortly thereafter, we entered the area and settled some distance away from the stage up a moderate hill so we could have a good view of the stage without being too close to the giant speakers placed near it. The sides of the stage were adorned with giant video screens on which the concert was supposed to be projected. Our spot seemed pretty decent.

People continued swarming into the park, mostly youngsters and teens. I looked for people my age. I think we all have this tendency to look for people like us. Either way, there were not many.

The area filled up quickly. The hill behind us, which up until a few minutes ago looked like a picturesque meadow, was fully occupied. We were surrounded by masses of people with zero distance between us, like fortythousand sardines in a can. Youngsters still migrated from place to place, trying to find the best vintage point or reunite with friends. This made them bump into others and even step on people's feet as they moved around. Not pleasant, yet I was impressed by the crowd's patience and understanding. It annoyed me at times, but I did not say a word. I understood the youngsters' need to move around.

I brought a plastic crate with me from the dairy so we could stand on it and improve our vantage point. My kids sat on the lawn, but I had a hard time sitting so low, so I used it as a chair until the concert began. When the music finally started, it filled the air with excitement as people applauded. Everyone stood up at once. The girl in front of me, who until that point sat on her beach chair, stood on top of it right when the concert started and blocked my view almost entirely. I protested slightly, but my voice drowned in the hubbub. I found a new vantage point from which I could see the large video screen well. When I stood on my tiptoes and stretched my neck to the maximum, I could see the stage with Paul and his band as miniscule figures.

I was glad Bat-El stood on the plastic crate. She is not particularly tall, and that gave her a perfect perspective. Every so often, we switched, especially when I felt a little out of air and sandwiched by the crowd. When your head is above everyone else's, you feel extremely lucky. First off, you can see beyond people's heads and second, there is air everywhere. The breeze that blew above us was refreshing and rejuvenating. I felt this amazing sense of flotation standing that tall above everyone.

Standing that long made me tired. My legs hurt. I felt them and realized they were very swollen. I already knew that swelling was a result of my lymphatic system's deficiency. I sat on the crate for a little bit and massaged my legs in order to encourage the lymphatic fluid up toward the heart, but the lack of oxygen and the sour smell that surrounded me when my head was the height of people's waistlines forced me to get up on my feet again.

The concert itself with the audience dynamics was amazing. It was nice to share this experience with two of my children. When some songs moved us in particular, I held Bat-El close and we shared a special embrace. We shared some deeply intimate moments with Orr, too.

Paul dedicated the song "My Love" to his late wife Linda, who died of cancer in 1998. He also moved the crowd with a few words in Hebrew. He sang "Something" in memory of George Harrison, who also died of cancer in 2001, and the song "A Day in the Life" in memory of John Lennon. Those moments were emotional. The cameraman caught a rare image of a young woman who was moved to tears, projected on the giant video screens. The crowd roared once more. I felt a chill up my spine. I wondered: *The man (McCartney) has reached the top of his professional career, is very rich but is surrounded by the death of his loved ones. How does he live with himself? Is he lonely? Is he happy?* From my perspective, thirty meters from the stage, I felt like he was one of us—flesh and blood, seeking, as we all do, some attention and love from the audience.

Philosophical thoughts about the meaning of life came to mind. *Here I am, alive and well, with enough stamina and inspiration to go out with my kids, when I could have easily been among the dead, had the circumstances been slightly different. I feel like I am on the winning side today. I am just like any ordinary person and even more. Unlike before, I am no longer jealous of healthy people. On the contrary. Few are the people like me, who have earned their life back after nearly been robbed of it.*

I do not know what it is exactly that sets me apart from so many other patients who have not survived and parted this world with great agony. I keep wondering what has made the difference in my case. What is the recipe that has allowed me to overcome and survive? I feel like I thoroughly understand the dynamics of prostate cancer, yet cannot give others a recipe that will allow them to achieve the same goals if they only follow it. There is no doubt I am lucky, yet I am well aware that there is no guarantee, and this scum or another can attack once more without prior notice. In that sense, I am no different than anybody else. We are all exposed to life's dangers.

Toward the end of the concert, Paul sang the song "Live and Let Die," with amazing special effects like fire, smoke, and fireworks filling up the stage. The crowd was in ecstasy. It was, no doubt, the high point of the night, at least technologically. The entire stage seemed as if it were going up in flames, but as soon as the song ended, the fire and smoke disappeared and things went back to normal.

The audience did not let Paul off the stage. Eventually, he said in Hebrew with a thick British accent, "You have to go home," and the crowd answered unanimously, "No!" This went on several times.

After the concert was over, we followed the crowds to the train station. There was a sense of spiritual uplift in the air, not just with us. I heard other people expressing their heightened feelings.

At the train station and outside, there were crowds of people coming out of Paul's performance, and everyone wanted to go home. A few trains left but the docks were still crowded and the crowds were almost unbearable

Finally, after being thoroughly exhausted, we reached the train that waited on the platform. It was so crowded that we did not manage to stay together and were pushed into separate cars. Luckily, we had cell phones and I could verify that both my children were on the train. The train was so packed that I remained standing. I felt extremely tired and could not wait to reach the car so I could finally sit down.

We got off at Beit Yehosha train station, where our car was parked, climbed into our car, and began to drive north. It was nearly one in the morning. We were hungry. I remembered there was a local restaurant near Haifa that was open all night. We stopped there and we each ate two savory pastries and drank some coffee to shake off the fatigue.

Despite the coffee, I felt too tried to go on driving, so I let Orr drive, though he was not covered as a driver on my insurance policy. We got home at three in the morning. Exhausted.

As I took a shower, I thought of the Beatles song Paul McCartney sang at the concert.

"It's been a hard day's night..."

EPILOGUE

December 2016

Eight years have passed since this book was first published in Hebrew, and I am celebrating fifteen years since I was first diagnosed with terminal illness and the medical establishment gave me two years to live.

In the eight years that have passed a lot more has happened:

I have reached my sixty-fifth year, my hair has turned gray, I have some new lines on my face, but my body has remained in top shape. My medical indices are just short of perfect, though it is clear that the scum has not deserted me and continues to follow me like a shadow. I continue what I call maintenance treatments, nothing too dramatic.

My relationship with Rivka has ended. I suppose that as a couple, we could no longer contain the countless events that flooded us during those years, and we have gone our separate ways.

Our three children have all grown up, left the house in Mitzpe Hila, and are busy with their own lives. We recently had the pleasure of seeing our daughter Bat-El marry her beloved, a charming young man named Yotam.

I share my life with a princess named Anat, who has moved into my home in Mitzpe Hila along with her young daughter. While it takes me fifteen years back to when Rivka and I were happily raising our own adolescents, it is not an easy challenge, and I am using all of my social skills to get through it pleasantly and fairly.

After twenty-one years in the dairy, in which we saw it succeed financially, I bid my farewell and sold my share in the company to my partner. The compensation I received allows me not to work for a living.

I look back at the list of things I have accomplished/will probably accomplish/will probably not accomplish that I prepared during my chemotherapy (see Chapter Eight) I am happy to say that most of the goals I set forth on my list, including those under the column "will probably not accomplish," have been fulfilled above and beyond expectations.

The doctors I have crossed paths with, most of whom treated me with great devotion, have grown older and are ready to retire. Some have already retired and, sadly, two of them have passed away.

From a medical standpoint, the years that have passed have brought with them an impressive progress in terms of prostate cancer treatments, especially with regards to diagnosing and treating metastasized prostate cancer. These blessed developments reassure me that should the scum attack again, I will have the tools to fight it in the future, as well.

My life is abundant. You can say that God has stood by me during the fifteen years that I have been sick, though I believe I have also done a great deal on my part. When I think about it, I can sum up the insights I have adopted over the years, with regards to coping with cancer or other crises, in a way that may help other patients significantly.

Made in the USA
Coppell, TX
06 June 2023

17769032R00157